THE SMALL WORLD OF FRED HOYLE

Also by Fred Hoyle

NOVELS

The Black Cloud
Ossian's Ride
October the First is Too Late
A for Andromeda } *with J. Elliot*
Andromeda Breakthrough } *with J. Elliot*
Fifth Planet } *with G. Hoyle*
Rockets in Ursa Major } *with G. Hoyle*
Seven Steps to the Sun } *with G. Hoyle*
The Molecule Men } *with G. Hoyle*
The Inferno } *with G. Hoyle*
Into Deepest Space } *with G. Hoyle*
The Incandescent Ones } *with G. Hoyle*
The Westminster Disaster } *with G. Hoyle*
Comet Halley

PLAY

Rockets in Ursa Major

NON-FICTION

Some Recent Researches in Solar Physics
The Nature of the Universe
A Decade of Decision
Frontiers of Astronomy
Astronomy
Of Men and Galaxies
Galaxies, Nuclei and Quasars
Man in the Universe
From Stonehenge to Modern Cosmology
Nicolaus Copernicus
Highlights in Astronomy
Astronomy Today
Ten Faces of the Universe
Stonehenge
The Cosmogony of the Solar System
The Intelligent Universe
Lifecloud } *with N.C. Wickramasinghe*
Diseases from Space } *with N.C. Wickramasinghe*
Commonsense and Nuclear Energy *with G. Hoyle*

THE SMALL WORLD OF FRED HOYLE

AN AUTOBIOGRAPHY

MICHAEL JOSEPH LONDON

First published in Great Britain by Michael Joseph Ltd
27 Wrights Lane, Kensington, London W8

British Library Cataloguing in Publication Data

Hoyle, Fred
The small world of Fred Hoyle: an
autobiography.
1. Hoyle, Fred   2. Astronomers — Great
Britain — Biography
I. Title
520′.92′4   QB36.H75
ISBN 0-7181-2740-4

Typeset by Alacrity Phototypesetters,
Banwell Castle, Weston-super-Mare
Printed and bound in Great Britain by
Billing & Sons Limited, Worcester

CHAPTER ONE

MY FATHER always wore a trilby hat. It wasn't anything to do with the weather, because until his later years he worked bareheaded in his garden. Yet for the short step into the local village of Gilstead, for a walk to the town of Bingley a mile away, and certainly for business in the bigger city of Bradford, he always wore a trilby hat.

This male fashion would only be a minor shift of custom from the 1920s to the present day if it were not for the large size, to the modern eye, of those hats. The effect of wearing a brimmed hat rather than a close-fitting bonnet is to make the head look bigger. If you were suddenly transported back to the 1920s the difference that would surely hit you with the force of an executioner's axe would be that everybody walking the streets would appear to have heads twice as large as we see them today. Here, in one move, we have the reason why it is so difficult to notice the circumstances and events in one's own day that will appear remarkable, important and even amazing in the future. No commentator in the 1920s would have thought to record the size of trilby hats. If it hadn't been for the existence of the camera, this really quite big shift in human psychology would be well on its way to becoming lost. Why did people in the 1920s want to make their heads seem so big? Or to put it from their point of view, why do we today want to make our heads seem so small?

The River Aire rises in limpid pools in limestone hills near the village of Malham, which because of its beauty was always a mecca for my parents. After passing Skipton, which I suppose means sheeptown, the Aire opens into a wide valley filled with sediments that extend as far as Keighley. Continuing downriver a further three or four miles, the valley narrows into a bottleneck at the town of Bingley. Thereafter it opens out again in a flattish bottom at Shipley, where it continues nearly eastward to Leeds, and thence eventually out via the River Humber to the sea.

People commanding a strategic bottleneck traditionally live by exacting tribute from travellers and traders, and so it seems to have been with Bingley as far back as the Domesday Book. In industrial times, traders plying their wares between the agricultural communities of the Wharfe Valley around Ilkley and Otley and the early manufacturing centre of the Halifax district took care to steer clear of both Bingley and Shipley – the latter probably because of swamps, the former because of rapacity. Their route is being imitated nowadays by modern motorists. It went over Ilkley Moor and down through the village of Eldwick to Gilstead. Here it turned into Primrose Lane to avoid Bingley, passing immediately before the very door of the house where I would be born. The community of Bingley responded to this scheme by doing its worst to convert Primrose Lane into a quagmire. The tug-of-war from Domesday down the centuries culminated in July 1758, when an indictment was made against the inhabitants of Bingley, for the solid reasons that the King's subjects could not 'go, return, pass, ride and labour without great danger of their lives and loss of their goods [wherefore] the inhabitants of the parish of Bingley shall repair and amend when and so often as it shall be necessary the Common Highway aforesaid [Primrose Lane] so as aforesaid being in decay'.

The bottleneck of Bingley had more valid commercial advantages during the second half of the nineteenth century. Its importance continued, but with the bang gradually fading to a whimper, through my boyhood. The steep sides of the Aire Valley offered sources of water power for textile mills which provided the main employment for the outlying villages of Morton on my side of the valley, and of Harden, Cullingworth and Haworth on the western side. There were sheep in plenty on the hill farms on both sides of the valley, with spinning mills close by, a way of life that formed the background to the novels of the Brontë sisters. You could see their village of Haworth from my village of Gilstead. For that matter, you could see Brontë country from my bedroom window.

Gilstead wasn't a place of manufacture, however. In my boyhood there couldn't have been more than two or three hundred village people, earning their livings in diverse ways. There was a big quarry supplying stone to Bingley, of which my maternal grandfather, William Pickard, had been the foreman. He died in his early thirties long before I was born, apparently from silicosis, although it wasn't called that in those days. In addition to rising from stonemason to quarry foreman, William Pickard, by the time of his early death, had built a house for himself and his young wife, my maternal grandmother. Had he lived, my mother would surely not have had to work for so long in the local mill to earn the money that took her eventually to the Royal Academy of Music in London.

There were two farms, Walsh's and Robinson's, around which my youth revolved. There were a few substantial properties and the more modest houses of folk like my father who worked down in the Aire Valley itself. One of the substantial properties had a determining effect on my life – the Milnerfield Estate. A mystery surrounded this estate, a mystery which still persists to this day.

I never had sight nor sound of any member of the Salt family, which was the nearest thing to divinity I ever heard of in my youth. The Salt family owned the Milnerfield Estate. The Salt family had a big textile mill down where the Aire Valley broadens into the Shipley region. The family built houses close to the mill for its employees, and the conglomerate ultimately became so large that it formed a township in its own right, known as Saltaire. The Milnerfield Estate stretched all the way up the valley from the lowlands around Saltaire to the highlands around Gilstead. Where the estate abutted the village, a stone wall fully ten feet high was built. The remarkable thing about this stone wall was that its construction was so precise, stone fitting exactly on stone in a manner the ancient Incas would have approved of, that at no point was even the most agile village boy able to climb it. In my youth we made hundreds and hundreds of attempts, but never once did anyone manage to 'swime', as we said, on top of the big, overhanging flagstones which capped the wall.

Nearest to the village was a narrow lane about six feet wide, with the Great Wall of Milnerfield on one side and a dark strip of woodland on the other, the woodland also being enclosed by walls, so that you went along the lane between high walls on both sides. We called it the 'Sparable', but later in life I learned that its proper name was the Sparrow's Bill. Even on a bright day it was dark along the Sparrow's Bill, and since there were many twists and turns to it you had the impression that an ogre was waiting around the next corner, an ogre from which it would be impossible to escape because of the walls on either side. It was by forcing myself to go alone along the

Sparrow's Bill at night that somewhere about the age of seven I learned not to be afraid of the dark.

The perimeter of the Milnerfield Estate remote from the village was more readily negotiated, even though the wall was everywhere well constructed and fairly smooth. The estate was no small affair, by the way. Before the outlying farms were sold off it was an extensive block of land that lay strategically athwart the ancient traders' route between the Wharfe and Aire Valleys. But to proceed with my personal story. The trouble from our point of view was that low wages permitted a truly great number of gardeners and gamekeepers to be employed, so that except by using real guile you could hardly make a hundred yards inside the place without having a brawny adult seize you by the ear and march you at the double to one of the exits. In retrospect, the geomorphological cunning of us village boys fills me with admiration, for really it couldn't have been better done. We realised that since the estate was on a general downslope, water had inevitably to flow through the wall. There was one particular place along the Sparrow's Bill where the masons had left a low hole in the wall to permit the passage of a stream, and provided the stream wasn't in flood an agile young boy or girl could just squeeze through without becoming too seriously wet. This was our point of attack in exploring the Milnerfield Estate. One day we came on a partridge's nest with perhaps fifteen brown eggs in it. We hadn't been admiring the nest for more than a minute or so before a gamekeeper came roaring down on us with a threatening stick. I can't vouch for the intention of the other lads, but I know I had no particular intention of seizing the eggs. It was the sheer beauty of the nest which impressed me, to a point where I can still conjure a vision of it to this day.

I was never a great one for taking eggs from birds' nests, for the reason that I could see no interest in them once they were taken. If you blew them there was only an empty shell that did nothing, and if you didn't blow them they soon started to smell terribly. I found it far more interesting to watch what happened if you left the eggs where they were. On one occasion when I was scouting alone I found a kingfisher's nest along the banks of the same stream by which we entered the Milnerfield Estate. I told one of the lads about it; whether he took the eggs or someone else did I never knew. When I found the nest empty it seemed an absurd waste. Here had been something which would make marvellously coloured birds that were not to be.

Strange events were in train at the Milnerfield Estate, an almost literal enactment of the first part of the story of *Sleeping Beauty.* The practice in my early boyhood was for the managing director of the Salts' textile mill to live at Milnerfield House, from which he drove daily to and from the mill in a horse-drawn carriage along a mile of driveway, on the sides of which the grass was mown meticulously by hand. But the house itself was a grim pile indeed, designed by some more than usually insane architect in a fashion that would have done credit to the stories of Edgar Allan Poe. And grim stories were rife in the village as to what went on in the house, stories which delighted my young ears, I can tell you. Deaths and disasters, ghosts and ghouls – no good ever came to anybody who lived there. When I was about nine years old it fell out just as the old ladies of the village said it would. Just as the princess in *Sleeping Beauty* pricked herself on a spindle, so the managing director of the Salts' textile mill pricked himself on a thorn bush. Within hours, blood-poisoning had set in, and within a week a hearse was carrying his coffin down the mile-long driveway to the cemetery in Saltaire. The gardeners and gamekeepers melted away. Nobody ever came to live there again. Grass grew thick down the carriageway, the splendidly cultivated gardens and orchards fell more and more into disuse, more and more of the greenhouse windows were broken due to chance events, and above all the house simply fell down, to be carted away stone by stone, until today there is literally nothing but a place left for sixty years to become a jungle – just like the environs of the castle in *Sleeping Beauty*.

There was a time early in the century when it was very much otherwise, when the estate looked as if it might swallow the village itself. Four houses known as 'Milnerfield Villas' were built outside the high wall to accommodate the highest-ranking servants – the butler, the head gardener and so on. They were substantially built, as estate agents say, a step ahead in quality of most of the other houses in the village. In 1910, a decision was taken to reverse this process. The houses, including the four known as Milnerfield Villas, were sold, probably because it was found that estate folk didn't mix with village folk. I have a fair idea why. When I was about eight, apparently during some crisis at the estate, a footman erupted from the big iron gates that guarded the entrance to its carriageway, and then rushed with a bundle of letters to the village post office. I remember nothing of the man's appearance, but I do remember as if it were yesterday that he was wearing white gloves. In a derisive gang we followed him to and from the post office, dogging his heels as closely as we dared. Since white gloves and earthy village life obviously didn't mix, the estate decided to sell its scattered properties outside the big, flagstone-capped wall. And my mother decided that somehow, someplace, she would raise the money to buy the residence at the lower end with the high-sounding address of 4, Milnerfield Villas. It was there that on 24 June 1915 I was born.

It wasn't the high-sounding address my parents had wanted. It was the view. From number four you can see over the flagstone-capped wall into the kitchen-garden and orchard of the estate. More relevant, however, the eye lifted to the summit of a moor two miles away,

Rombald's Moor to give its official name, although nobody local ever called it anything but Baildon Moor. The point is that with astute use of Ordnance Survey maps you can walk from the summit of Rombald's Moor to the outskirts of Edinburgh without ever descending even into a village, sleeping at night only in remote farmsteads. If at Edinburgh you take David Balfour's route across the Firth of Forth and thence beyond the Highland line, you can continue through remote places to the end of Britain at Cape Wrath. So throughout my youth at 4, Milnerfield Villas, I had half-a-thousand miles of open country beckoning me everlastingly towards adventure.

Owen Glendower says to Hotspur:

> . . . at my nativity
> The front of heaven was full of fiery shapes,
> Of burning cressets; and at my birth
> The frame and huge foundation of the Earth
> Shaked like a coward.

So it was at my own birth, the fiery shapes and the shaking of the Earth being caused by the thundering guns of armies locked in the battles of the First World War. My father was already in his mid-thirties when the First World War broke out in 1914. Shortly after I was born, he was conscripted into the British Army, choosing to opt for the Machine Gun Corps, which choice he said in after years was dictated by his dislike of 'bull'. The life expectancy of machine gunners was so short that 'bull' was not demanded of them. Nor were machine gunners likely to be accused of insubordination, a risk which an infantryman of thirty-five holding strong views about the intelligence of his senior commanders might easily have been exposed to.

So it came about that my mother and I were left alone to live on fivepence a day, the government allowance to the wives of soldiers serving a country that needed them so much, according to General Kitchener. Had it not been for me, my mother could have returned to her former job of school teaching. But with me so very young, and of a somewhat frail disposition I believe, she felt a job which avoided leaving me during the daytime was to be preferred, if it could be found. During the first years of the century my mother had worked in a Bingley mill, as I mentioned earlier. With the money she saved, and with help from her own mother and elder sister, she had then studied music at the Royal Academy. The outcome was a training and a qualification which permitted her to embark on a career as a professional singer. Times were hard, as they always seem to be for young musicians, so my mother was tempted out of full-time professional work to teach music in schools. Her career was blocked, however, in 1911 when she married, because in those days married women were not employed as teachers, although during the war years the rule was held temporarily in abeyance.

Even before 1911 my mother had begun transferring her main interest from singing to the piano. From my earliest memories to her death forty years later she hardly ever passed a day without spending two or three hours at the piano. The solution to the problem of a job in 1916, therefore, lay literally to hand – to go out of an evening and play the musical accompaniment to silent films at a cinema in the town of Bingley. I was put to bed in my mother's bed and off she would go leaving me to fall asleep, which I did without difficulty until I reached the age of two. My earliest memory is of lying awake for a while and wondering what I would do if my mother never came back. Then I cried for a bit and at last went off to sleep. There were two teenage girls next door, Ethel and Mary Clark, but it seems that when they came round to sit with me I said I was all right alone.

Eventually my mother lost her job at the local cinema

because her musical tastes did not suit those of its manager. Her idea of accompanying films was to play parts of Beethoven sonatas. Imagine whooping Indians charging soundlessly in jerky black and white, done with the execrable cinematographic technique of 1917, accompanied by the thunderous roll of the third movement of the Moonlight Sonata. About a week after my mother's dismissal, however, there came a tap on the front door of the house. It was the manager come to ask my mother to return to her job. After she'd left there had been a decline in attendances. On enquiry around the town the man had been told, 'We didn't come to see your films, we came to hear Mrs Hoyle play.'

The early development of musical appreciation made it impossible for me to learn to play a musical instrument myself. To a young child of two who knew how the Waldstein Sonata goes, the trite pieces one must play to learn a musical instrument seemed indescribably boring. The gap between appreciation and achievement had become too large to be bridged. Learning comes best if a child does not become too sophisticated too early on.

It turned out better where numbers were concerned. With much time on her hands during the day my mother taught me the numbers, and almost immediately I began to set little problems for myself. I was coming up to three years old when one morning I asked my mother if two sixes made twelve. She answered yes, and then asked me how I knew. I can't claim I remember my answer, but from its reported nature I think it has to be true, since an adult would hardly have thought of arguing like this: 'One and six make seven, so two and six make eight, so three and six make nine, so four and six make ten, so five and six make eleven, so six and six make twelve.' By remembering my previous results and using the same slow but sure method, I managed between the ages of three and four to construct a good deal of the multiplication tables for myself. The reason for the plodding method was simply that I worked in my head after being put to bed at night.

The life expectancy of a British machine gunner in the First World War was only three or four months. It was inevitable then that every day my mother watched in dread for the arrival of the postman bearing the government's heartfelt regret that my father could serve as cannon fodder no longer. As each day passed without the arrival of a letter expressing the government's grief, it could only have seemed to my mother that the inevitable had been postponed for just a little longer.

As the days, weeks and months passed inexorably away with their grim toll on the Western Front, it was said with macabre humour by the men of the British Machine Gun Corps that there were two whom death could not touch: the two 'aitches, Holmes and Hoyle. Random chance, or luck as we say, always works to make it seem like that, and I daresay something of the same sort happened with fighter and bomber pilots in the Second World War. If the life expectancy of the average machine gunner was four months, there would be a lucky one among twenty who would survive for a whole year, a lucky one among four hundred who would survive for two years, and a lucky one among eight thousand who would survive for three years. As well as being lucky, my father had characteristics which must have aided his survival. He was compact in build with a bubbling sense of humour, very quick in sprint races, and with exceptionally keen eyesight. Since exceptionally keen eyesight must surely have been one of the really important advantages that a man in the trenches of the First World War could have had, quite likely Holmes was similarly endowed. But I never learned about Holmes because I don't think he and my father knew each other. And a day eventually came when their meeting became impossible, the day Holmes was killed. It was from then onwards that my father said he began to feel really bad, and suffered from the immovable conviction that for him too the time must surely be coming, just as after a long partnership in cricket both batsmen often fall to the bowlers in quick succession.

If my father had been lucky until March 1918, he was unlucky on the 21st of that month – unlucky to be exposed in the trenches on the day the German Chief of Staff, Erich Ludendorff, launched what is generally conceded to have been the fiercest assault of the whole war, 'Operation Michael' to use its code-name. An official history reads as follows: 'The launching of "Michael" took the British by surprise, but the ensuing Second Battle of the Somme did not develop as Ludendorff had expected. While the German Army south of the Somme achieved a complete breakthrough, the big attack to the north was held up by a heavy concentration of forces near Arras. For a whole week Ludendorff mistakenly persisted in trying to carry through his original plan in the north, instead of exploiting the unexpected success in the south ...' Here in only a few words you have an overall distant view of the situation. But what actually happened there on the ground?

I never heard my father say exactly where his post was located and I doubt that he really knew, because almost surely he wasn't issued with a map, although he had long been the leader of a machine gun crew of eight men. But from his description, never put together in one piece but coming out on odd occasions over the years, it is likely my father's post was in the Somme Valley, in the south where Ludendorff made his unexpected breakthrough.

There is at least one semi-official history of the British Machine Gun Corps. The writer says that very little is known of what happened to machine gunners in the Somme Valley on 21 March 1918, because few of them survived the day. According to the writer there was a thick morning mist. At first light the German field command sent patrols, amply equipped with stick grenades, through the mist. Because of the mist the machine gunners were caught unawares and were almost completely taken out, mostly without firing a round in their own defence. In just a few spots, the writer says, a capricious swirl of mist happened to clear the ground, permitting the machine gunners to see ahead to open fire effectively, and so to save themselves. If I believed this story I would have to suppose that my father's life, which as a result of his survival made a big difference to my own life, turned on a capricious swirl of heavy morning mist. But there was more to the matter, issues which either the writer of the semi-official history did not know about, or did not wish to discuss. The question this history actually raises is how the German patrols made their way through thick mist and managed to take out the British machine gun positions so unerringly. I happen to know the likely answer to this question. It was because the leaders of British machine gun posts were under orders at all times while in the front line to fire bursts at ten-minute intervals, to fire mostly, therefore, at nothing at all. Consequently the Germans knew from simple observation exactly where the British posts were located. Presumably the German patrols came through the mist on compass bearings. Knowing the exact direction and more or less the exact distance they had to go, they would perhaps walk at first and would then crawl the last yards until they heard voices.

The machine gun was the single most important ground-based weapon of the First World War, a crucial fact the British High Command never seems to have understood from the first day of the war to the last. By March 1918, Douglas Haig was Commander-in-Chief of the British forces in France. Haig had written in a report dated 1915 that he thought a ration of two or three machine guns to a battalion would be quite sufficient, which showed that, despite an already long career as a professional soldier, Haig had not understood the basic strategic lesson of the American Civil War of 1861-5 – namely, the astonishing extent to which a few posts equipped with even the crudest of early automatic weapons could hold up large numbers of infantrymen, always provided the posts were carefully concealed. Even riflemen in concealment, snipers as we call them nowadays, were effective in the field to a degree that officers in staff colleges could not believe, until during the First World War the fact was rediscovered in the hardest conceivable way, or, as in Haig's case, not rediscovered at all.

From the earliest days when he had become the leader of an eight-man machine gun crew, my father had ignored the order to fire random bursts at ten-minute intervals, telling his crew never to fire except on critical occasions. Although his ignoring of orders was probably dictated at first by thoughts of survival, practical observations in the field soon convinced him that his policy had to be correct. The Germans always went for machine guns first, which proved, as my father told me in later years, that the positioning of the guns was critical, at any rate in German eyes. Of course it was, because the machine gun more than anything else defined the nature of trench warfare, a truth it was possible to stumble on in practice, but a truth that remained perpetually hidden at British headquarters. Time and again British commanders sought to break German defences with heavy artillery barrages followed by advances of large numbers of infantry, only for the infantry to be mown down by German machine guns – thereby leading to those many letters that came daily through the British post expressing the heartfelt grief of a government which nevertheless maintained those who made these disastrous misjudgements in their posts, largely, I suppose, because summary dismissal would have been 'bad form'.

So it came about on 21 March 1918, when the German ground attack eventually came an hour or so after the activities of the stick bombers, that my father's post was still operating. Now indeed he had unprecedented luck. In an ordinary engagement, where every hundred yards of ground was bitterly contested, the loss of support on either side would have been disastrous. But the staggering magnitude of the German advance in the Somme Valley meant that the German infantry simply poured through the holes on either side of my father's position. Doubtless it would be the intention of some German officer to clear out the few still-active British machine guns in due course, but why bother for the moment when the way ahead was clear? So hell for leather the Germans went, at first in hundreds of yards, then in quarter miles, and at last in whole miles. Leaving a crew of eight men still alive, one a dazed, half-shell-shocked man approaching forty and the others recent recruits on the right side of twenty. Through his mental mist my father told me that he almost became convinced, because of the uncanny silence now fallen over the shattered British line, that he had indeed been killed and had passed into some grotesque new form of existence.

Towards evening his judgement of the situation gradually returned. After more than two years of practical experience, and with the keen sight I mentioned before, he had learned to judge battlefield situations, to judge where men were fighting, where guns were firing, and the lie of the land generally. At last he understood that the unbelievable had happened. As if aided by powers never seen before, the Germans had done what our official historian says they did: 'The German Army south of the Somme achieved a complete breakthrough.' Seeing how it was, my father explained things to his young crew, telling them there were two possibilities. They could stay put, with the prospect of being taken prisoner, or they could move back and try to penetrate the now greatly advanced German front from its rear. My father then said that in his physically shocked condition he didn't feel he could manage to crawl great distances across vile, crater-strewn ground. So he told each member of the crew to make their own decision. One of the crew, a young fresh-faced farmboy from Somerset, decided to stay with him. The others elected to try their luck.

It was a long, distressed night that followed, but in the way the human body sometimes does my father began to feel stronger towards dawn on the 22nd, so that eventually he was able to move. He and the farmboy from Somerset set off, not walking openly, of course, but edging from one depression to another. The problem was whether to try crawling through the German position, or to stay behind it, moving parallel to what had become an entirely new front in the hope of there being a gap somewhere along it. Not being an infantryman himself, it seemed better to trust to observation and geography rather than risk a tussle with German infantry. So it was a hole in the front, or nothing. After three days of crawling and dodging, a possible gap was found. A gap it turned out to be, and after a week, by 28 March or thereabouts, my father and the farmboy from Somerset rejoined the British concentration near Arras. He never saw the other six members of the crew again.

The war over, the British government showed considerable generosity to young officers, sending many of them free of charge to university. I never detected a comparable generosity in the treatment of ordinary war widows. In all cases known definitely to me, the sons of war widows left school at fourteen to earn what they could to support mothers in straitened circumstances. I cannot say this would necessarily have been my own fate had luck, sharp eyes and common sense not aided my father's return from France. My mother might, with her qualifications, have obtained a teaching job again, so that events for me could have fallen out not too differently from the way they actually were.

By the late summer of 1918, German prisoners were coming over in droves. They were ragged, half starved and desperately hungry. Rations were distributed to them in groups of ten, rations that were by no means generous. One day my father watched a group distributing its combined ration. One of the group was first elected by lot. The chosen man then divided the ration into ten portions as equally as he could manage. Thereafter the others drew lots among themselves as to how to distribute nine of the portions, leaving the last and tenth portion for the man who had done the division.

The German government put out peace feelers in 1916, but owing to the political confusion, from which no Allied leader emerged with credit, the German initiative came to nothing. This moment in 1916 was perhaps the crucial turning point of the twentieth century. Had there been peace in 1916, needless slaughter would have been stopped in the short term, and in the long term we would probably not have anything like the present day superpower confrontation, for the 1917 communist revolution in Russia would most likely not have happened either.

The year 1916 is not very far back in time, in the sense that it lies within the span of a single human lifetime. A visit to any major library would permit you to examine the issue of *The Times* for any day in 1916 you pleased. Yet so far at least as some aspects of technology are concerned, a single human lifetime has covered greater change than occurred in the whole of the preceding thousand years. The biggest social change, I believe, has been in communication. No young person today could, I think, conceive of a society in which there was an almost impenetrable barrier of communication on a day-to-day basis between government and the upper levels of society on the one hand, and the mass of ordinary people on the other. Notably, we have radio and television in most households today telling us of happenings, not just in

Britain and other developed countries, but in every corner of the world. We have newspapers available at a cost that can be sustained by most households. The cost of subscribing to *The Times* in 1916 amounted to half an ordinary man's wage. Aside from possibly at the Milner-field Estate, there would be no daily copy of *The Times* in our village, and probably not more than a dozen copies throughout the whole Bingley area. There was no radio or television, of course, so that news travelled literally by word of mouth. In the 1920s my father would bring a copy of the Bradford daily paper back home when he returned from business in the evening, but unless the skies fell in on a national or international basis our sources of news were intensely local. There were no opinion polls either, so governments were just as out of touch with ordinary people as ordinary people were out of touch with governments.

The almost instant formation of public opinion today, over issues the public would scarcely have heard of in 1916, constitutes one of the greatest changes the world has ever seen. Almost everyone today, except the media, agrees that they are a blessed nuisance, but the media have changed the world from one in which people could be trivially manipulated to one in which a catastrophe like the 1914–18 war has surely become impossible.

A visit to the Soviet Union is to be recommended for the insight it gives into the way things used to be. Most Western visitors experience a prison-house atmosphere there, an atmosphere which has nothing to do with actually being in prison. Your papers can be completely in order, you may even be a privileged visitor on some mission or other, and yet if you are at all sensitive to atmosphere you get the prison-house feeling within hours of arriving in Moscow. It comes, I think, from the communication barrier. The Russian people do not have our two-way communication with their government. There is just the same pall over present-day Russian national life that there used to be over ours. While nowadays people speak of a free world in the West, it is as well to remember that our freedom is, historically speaking, a very recent occurrence. My own memory easily goes back to days when it was not so, to days when ordinary people had no voice, days of easy manipulation for governments. Perhaps in another fifty years the same changes will have taken place in the Soviet Union. If so, a great cloud will have been lifted from the world as a whole, a cloud which descended on it in only the third year of my life.

Chapter Two

WHENEVER I SURVEY the modern scene with its special shops for the youngest children, playschools and TV programmes for somewhat older children, and free medical and dental care for all, the circumstances of my youth seem as far remote from the world in which a child grows up today as one might expect for two different planets revolving around quite different stars. I have to doubt, therefore, that much of what I can say of my own times will seem meaningful in a modern context, although it may conceivably have the virtue which comes with things long gone by, hopefully like a bottle of old wine one comes on unexpectedly in the corner of some cellar.

For balance and sophistication, for understanding how the world works, young people today are a decade ahead of where we were. Equate fifteen-year-olds today with twenty-five-year-olds in the 1920s and the comparison would be about right. Necessarily so, for without television, radio or newspapers in most households, we knew nothing of what was going on outside an area which literally was not more than a few miles across. You might think our deficiencies would have been put right at school, but the same parochial fog also hung over the schools, or at least over the schools I attended. Until I reached the upper forms of the local grammar school I do not think any teacher ever mentioned events on a national scale, still less on an international scale.

In its review of the year 1925 *The Times* began as follows:

> The year is likely to be remembered as that of Locarno, and the name Locarno may possibly be blessed by many generations. Such at least was the intention of the representatives of those nations which took part in the Pact initiated there and afterwards signed in London. The consummation of this agreement had involved much anxious and delicate negotiation, as susceptibilities had to be consulted and apprehensions allayed; and it had necessitated the retracing of impracticable but well-meant steps taken the year before. While it was recognized to be no more than a beginning it was confidently believed to have laid lasting foundations. In effect, the Pact bound France, Belgium and Germany, under guarantee of Great Britain and Italy, not to make war on one another, and ensured the inviolability of the frontiers concerned, subject to the reference of any outbreak of hostilities to the League of Nations, of which Germany was to become a member. The Pact also foreshadowed international arbitration and concerted measures towards disarmament.

Six weeks or so after this was published I took my junior scholarship examination, in curious circumstances I will describe later. If I'd been asked by the examiners to describe the Pact of Locarno I would have known as little about it as I did about the Diet of Worms. Imagine a similar situation today with an apparently permanent pact sealed, signed and delivered between the superpowers. The immense emphasis in the media would acquaint every child with what was going on. Yet the Pact of Locarno proved a load of rubbish, with exactly the opposite to what was intended eventually happening in the 1930s. Human nature does not change to the extent that it would be any different today. Unfortunately, nations act conspicuously in their own interest, and the devil take the hindmost. This is such a clear lesson of history that it is surprising how leader writers and commentators of all kinds go on generation after generation chasing the same old chimeras. By not knowing anything about it in my younger years we were spared from traps like this into which the responsible section of society fell so completely.

The modern generation is much better fed and clothed than we were. The feeding shows itself to the eye in stature. I eventually grew to a height of five feet nine, which in my time was a bit above average, but which today would be on the short side. There were no such things as vitamin pills in my youth, and fresh fruit was unknown for about four months every winter. Improved clothing has come partly with greater affluence and partly through technical innovations, among which the anorak and rubber boot are outstanding.

Mine was quite possibly the worst-shod generation there has been since the inception of the industrial age. In poorer times people had worn wooden clogs, often without stockings, a trick I tried out once or twice but could never master. You needed a curious shuffling motion to be able to make progress at anything like speed. In my early years I often watched older people loping about in clogs and the process never failed to astonish me. In rain you inevitably got your feet wet with clogs but, once indoors with bare feet, the circulation soon returned and within half an hour clogged persons would be dry again. With the prosperity engendered by the industrial revolution, the aim became to shut out the weather entirely from one's footgear by wearing whacking great boots. In my first two years at school everybody wore boots, summer and winter alike. Then in a flash it seemed boots were out and shoes were in, perhaps because some manufacturer had discovered how to produce shoes at significantly less cost than boots. The shoes were leather-soled and they didn't last long, especially with the sort of wear we gave them. So it came about that most children had holes in their shoes which let in the rain like so many sieves, with the consequence that in bad weather a considerable fraction of us sat in school for hours on end with cold feet. Nobody among my acquaintances had several pairs of shoes, which necessarily made the re-soling process irregular, even if one's parents could afford it. After re-soling you had a month or so of bliss with dry feet, then another month or more while the holes got worse and worse to the point where something just had to be done . . . and so on, round and round the repair cycle until the uppers disintegrated, a situation that was not unknown even by the time I reached university. I'll just bet that in those days as many as a third of undergraduates had a hole in the sole of one or other of their shoes.

I was never conscious of being grievously bothered by the shoe situation, but I was indeed conscious of the need for some garment like an anorak. There were no special school buses in those days. Between the ages of nine and eleven I had a walk to school of about a mile and a quarter, which in normal weather I enjoyed much better than riding in a bus. But there were icy cold days in winter when it was otherwise. The first mile of my journey lay exposed along a north-going road that afforded not the slightest shelter from the wind. Then you turned sharply at right angles into the shelter of a row of cottages, Brick Kiln Row if I remember aright, and beside a high wall which protected the garden of one of the better-off families in the Eldwick district. I can remember how my ears and temples used to thaw out when I reached this welcome protection. For many years afterwards I blamed these icy experiences for a hugely painful infection of the middle ear which I contracted at this time.

With the exception of whooping cough and scarlet fever, I suffered more or less all the standard diseases of childhood. Such things were generally as much an advantage as a disadvantage. You had three or four days of high temperature when the world seemed to be coming to an end, then a few days of pampering in bed, followed by a week off school, or perhaps by two glorious weeks if you could manage to swing it on credulous adults. The infection of the middle ear was something else altogether. It was a whole week of acute and unmitigated pain, day and night alike. Our doctor, Dr Crocker, came from time to time and looked sadly at me with his dark, spaniel-like eyes, but he might just as well have stayed away for all the good he did me. Today, given a suitable antibiotic, the thing would have been over and done with in only a few hours, probably even before the pain became acute. Eventually the eardrum burst and the pain was at last relieved. Dr Crocker said I'd been lucky the abscess had burst outwards.

There was a form of spelling test in schools known as dictation, which quite likely is still in use. The teacher simply read out some passage which you had to write down. In the years after the middle-ear infection I always listened with great care in dictation tests, which was probably necessitated by a hearing defect that either followed the middle-ear infection or had an alternative cause I will mention in a later chapter. I was not overtly aware of any considerable disability until my thirties, when the trouble gradually grew into a progressive deafness of the left ear that became a handicap at just the stage in my life when I was involved in science politics, with the unwelcome correlation that the higher the politics in which I was embroiled the worse the deafness became. There may be some who have succeeded in affairs of state despite deafness, but the disadvantage is so severe that such cases must be few and far between. My own disability was not in those days serious enough for me to fail to understand what was being said. The trouble in a committee is that if you have to listen carefully, thinking all the time to check you have the discussion right, you miss the sudden interventions on which swaying fellow committee members often depends. Just as you need to be born with keen eyes to be a good ball games player, with fine balance to be a gymnast, with sound heart and lungs and muscles to be a runner, so you need to be born with sharp ears to be a successful politician. I never met one myself who couldn't hear a pin drop on the other side of London.

Unless you had a taste for the cut and thrust of surgery the medical profession tended to be an unsatisfactory vocation in the distant days of my childhood, because there was so little that could be done effectively about most afflictions. The doctor had to wait for nature to take its course, hoping for abscesses to burst in the right direction, as in the case of Dr Crocker. Even as late as the early 1940s a medical friend who graduated from Cambridge in my year, and who became a public health officer in an inner city area, expressed his dissatisfaction at what he regarded as the well-nigh hopeless struggle against tuberculosis. The fact that tuberculosis, a scourge throughout the nineteenth century and in my youth, is today almost a vanished disease demonstrates another of the major revolutions of the present century. It seems, however, that no good ever comes in human affairs without accompanying ill effects. Dramatically increased medical skills have inevitably led to exploding world populations, a critical problem we are somehow managing to duck in our own time, but which is likely to prove one of the grimmer issues of the next century.

Although people in my youth lived under shadows which have since been lifted, they were not apprehensive about it. I recall a considerable outbreak of smallpox, in about 1927, I think. Few among my friends and acquaintances, young or old, rushed to be vaccinated. With modern media pressure, doctors in such a situation would be overwhelmed. There is little doubt that the media take a pernicious delight in whipping whole populations into terror over dangers much less than this smallpox outbreak of around 1927, dangers which often prove quite illusory. The young today will hardly be able to appreciate what a profound relief it would be to them if they could only shrug off the modern atmosphere of whipped-up hysteria over things which never happen. There was a bit of hysteria in my youth over spiritualism and ghosts which the press did its best to hammer us with. This made something of an issue out of walking along the Sparrow's Bill alone at night, but it was exciting stuff and you could stand up to the ghosts for yourself.

Occasionally, the shadows thickened. I remember walking into a mean house built on a slope half-way between the village of Gilstead and the town of Bingley. It was a back-to-back affair in a row fifty yards or more long, facing across a narrow street towards an exactly similar back-to-back row. A boy I'd known more as an acquaintance than as a friend had lived there, but he had died of cerebral meningitis. Together with other of his acquaintances I filed past the coffin, with the inevitable thought of 'there but for the grace of God . . .' and noting how little light came in through the two downstairs windows of the house.

My earliest medical memories predate by about a decade the popular television series *Dr Finlay's Casebook* based on the stories of A.J. Cronin. Dr Crocker did not come to our house in the fabulous bull-nosed Morris car in which Dr Finlay and his senior colleague rode around their practice, because the bull-nosed Morris was still a vision for the future. Dr Crocker must have come by pony and trap, just as we had deliveries of fresh milk from Walsh's farm twice daily by pony and trap. A bull-nosed

Morris would indeed have been well-nigh useless, because the roads were unmade and full of potholes. I have a vision, again from around 1927, of a Sunbeam car lurching from pothole to pothole through the village. It must have been about this time that a private bus service was started. It went from Bingley through Gilstead as far as the nearby village of Eldwick. It always travelled with an open tailgate, where there were two or three steps, which passengers climbed to a height of about four feet above the road. What with the hills and potholes, there were sections where the bus travelled so slowly that you could easily slide yourself on to this step affair, which being at the back was hidden from the driver's view. Then the bus picked up speed and you hung on for dear life until you came to another slow spot close to your destination, when you dropped off again for dear life onto *terra firma.* We village boys appreciated this free service, and we always had a pleasant word for the owner driver. 'Aye, Mr Murgatroyd,' we would say.

The potholed road through Gilstead must have been pretty bad ten years earlier in the wartime years, for in late 1918 roadmen appeared with a big steamroller. I know this was so because somebody from the village came one afternoon and told my mother I had been standing watching the steamroller for upwards of two hours, and that I couldn't be shifted away from it. Doubtless the visitor thought me peculiar, but for myself I like to believe that already at the age of two and a half I'd demonstrated what my métier in life was going to be: an observer of the world and a ponderer on its problems. I cannot claim to remember this incident of the steamroller. I am simply reporting what was said to me in after years. Many people do claim, however, to have memories from their earliest years. It has never seemed to me wise social policy to challenge claims of this sort, but I am very doubtful of their accuracy. I doubt that any of us remembers with any clarity at all what happened to us before the age of five. The misapprehension comes from confusing later memories, which are real, with earlier events. This indeed is an issue over which the poorer one's memory happens to be the easier it is to be deceived. The brain seems at the age of five to more or less wipe itself clean of earlier memories, 'clearing store' in computer language, in preparation, presumably, for sterner times ahead. I suspect that only the memory of things one continues to do by rote on a day-to-day basis passes unimpaired through the age of five. Probably this is the real reason why education begins formally at five.

I have precise memories of things that happened to me at the age of six. On my sixth birthday I went for a walk with my parents and said: 'In another year I'll be *seven*!' I even know the exact bit of road we were walking when I said it, and I remember comparing unfavourably the boyishness of my bare knees with the manly long trousers my father was wearing, the itch to grow up quickly becoming almost ungovernable.

In contrast to this sharp clarity, such early memories as I believe I have float insubstantially in my mind. My earliest vague recollection is of standing outside the village church and of a bell ringing. Since the village church never had a bell of its own, the bell would have had to have been brought there for the occasion, which probably fixes the incident as occurring on 11 November 1918, the occasion of the armistice at the end of the First World War. It was probably announced by a sort of town crier who had come up from Bingley. From out of a distant fog I also seem to remember being given a small trinket to mark the occasion.

One has to be cautious not to confuse true memories with what we are told later by parents and friends of the family. An incident which I feel sure my parents would hardly have thought to talk about in later years occurred when I was about four. I always got up first in the mornings, as young children mostly do. For some reason

I sat down one morning on the carpet. Perhaps it was to look at stamps on letters which the postman had just delivered. I put down a hand on the carpet, to receive the shock of my young life. This shock happened to repeat itself a year or so ago in the garden of a pub where I was eating an evening meal in failing light. I had put my hand on a crawling wasp and had been stung for my carelessness. The recent case verified my impression that the experience was fairly traumatic, which I suppose is why I remember it.

My parents told me in later years that I discovered how to tell the time when coming up to the age of four. Here I have to be careful not to confuse the later information from my parents with the impression I have of the actual moment of discovery itself. There is a detail, however, in my apparent memory that only I would have known. So probably there is some substance to the memory. Since the incident was my first bit of research there would also be a reason for it to have stuck. It happened like this.

One of the things my father did immediately after being demobilised early in 1919 was to fix an old grandfather clock which ticked away boldly for years thereafter in a corner of our 'sitting room', as we called it in unashamedly middle-class terminology. For a while the grandfather clock was a talking point between my parents and between my father and others who came into the house to help him with it. I became more and more intrigued, and frustrated I suppose, by this thing which everybody around me called 'time'. Where *was* 'time', I asked myself. I hunted around trying to find it. Eventually, when the clock began to work, the mystery partially resolved itself. 'Time' had to do with the hands of the clock, which being a grandfather clock were quite obvious to the eye. Yet as one mystery became a little clearer others took its place. 'Time' was never the same twice running – which made you think a bit, didn't it?

Whatever 'time' was, it had to do with the motion of

the hands. I knew this to be true, an easy deduction, because one of my parents would ask, 'What's the time?' Then the other would look at the hands of the clock and give the answer. Not to be outdone, I got into the way of asking, 'What's the time?' My repeating of the question must have seemed inane, and it is to my parents' credit that they kept on answering it, for if they hadn't I would never have made my little discovery.

I'd been put to bed one night, but even then I contrived to shout downstairs, audibly in our house: 'What's the time?' One of my parents answered: 'Twenty past seven, and that's the last time.' If it was to be the last question for the day, there was nothing left but to think a bit before I went off to sleep. An idea suddenly occurred to me. Could it be that 'time', instead of being a mysterious number unknown to me called twenty past seven, was really two separate numbers, twenty and seven? Discoveries mostly need two steps, just as a tune needs an answering refrain. A second idea hit me almost immediately. There were two hands on the clock. Perhaps one number belonged to one hand and the other number belonged to the other hand. A few more repetitions of the question 'What's the time?' the following day showed that this was indeed so. Because the numbers on the clock face were big and clear, it was easy now to see there were two sets of them. One hand went with one set and the other hand went with the other set. Refinements remained, like the meaning of 'past' and 'to', but to all intents and purposes the problem was solved and I could turn to other puzzling things, like what made the wind blow.

The other memory I think I can claim to be genuine was also connected with the weather. I have a memory of being taken out sledging in winter by an older boy whose parents were friends of my parents. This must have been before I reached the age of five, since then I was allowed to go out by myself. We sledged on the roads, which provided a harder under-surface than open country would have done, permitting our sledges to have quite narrow steel runners. In a good year you could sledge down Primrose Lane, the ancient trading route which ran past our house, for about a mile until it reached a hump-backed bridge over the Leeds-to-Liverpool canal. This was about half-way down into the Aire Valley. Indeed you could go further if you could be bothered to pull your sledge two or three hundred yards over level ground from the canal bridge to the railway bridge, but we preferred to walk back up to the village again. We developed what we called a 'track', a band of hard-packed snow which you could go down at a fair old lick, the sort of thing modern skiers would call the 'piste'. To a modern eye the road was narrow and since it had quite high stone walls on either hand our track bore some similarity to the Cresta Run, had anybody in the village known of the Cresta Run. We lads had our own individual sledges and we went on them head-first. You went with your cap turned around with its peak to the back in the fashion of a catcher in baseball. Nothing of this would have been possible, of course, if there had been cars on the road.

The principle hazard was the other sledgers coming up the track, and we were perpetually shouting cries of warning to them. Going head-first at a fairish speed between high stone walls must have looked a little dangerous, and at a distance in time I'm surprised my parents allowed it. They did so, I suppose, because this was the way things had been for as long as they could remember. Actually, the procedure was safer than it looked. The head projected six inches at the front and the whole of the legs projected at the back. With the toes you could brake a bit, and by combining hand-pressure on the front of the sledge with the toes pushing on the ground it was possible to steer with commendably high precision (another process, by the way, that didn't do our shoes much good). I only came to grief once, and then because I was unwise enough to tackle a hill when it was almost completely iced. Soon seeing the danger of getting out of control, I edged to where there was snow near one of the walls and managed to stop with nothing worse than a bit of scraping against the wall. My sight when I was seven or eight was still good, and I liked sledging because it was the one physical activity where I was on a par with the village boys. I was always slower at running, less strong, and not too sparkling at ball games either.

These sledging episodes come into the area of clear memory. So too does an event which from extraneous evidence must have occurred when I was coming up to eight, which is to say in the spring of 1923. I lived not much more than a mile from Shipley Glen, a place recently designated to carry a motorway, which has caused much controversy. The Glen is a V-shaped ravine cut by a stream that drains from the slopes of the famous Ilkley Moor, where you do not go without a hat if you are wise. Many hundreds of hours of my youth were spent playing all manner of games in Shipley Glen. Every Easter Monday a fair was held on a wide stretch of open ground immediately to the north of the ravine, attended wet or fine by folk who mostly walked from the chain of small industrial towns lying between Bingley and Bradford.

My father had, as I said in the previous chapter, exceptionally good sight, the kind Americans call 'twenty–thirty vision' (seeing at thirty paces what you are normally supposed to see at twenty). Combined with good eye-to-hand control, he could play precision games like billiards and darts with great facility. It was his wont, whenever we attended either the fair in Shipley Glen or any other in the district, to win prizes at the darts stalls. Eventually their owners drove him off with a fury born of despair. 'Tha's 'ad *enough*,' they would shout after him. If my memory serves me right the prizes were mostly cheap crockery, which thereafter my mother had to suffer against her natural inclinations.

What was exceptional about the fair in 1923 was that I also won two prizes. My game was a ball-and-bucket affair. The balls were small, hard and highly elastic in their properties, while the buckets were wide-mouthed and shallow. The buckets, moreover, were carefully tilted to make nearly sure that a ball thrown into any one of them would immediately bounce out again, in which case you won no prize. However, if you were lucky enough to throw a ball so that it skimmed the inside of a bucket, going round and round like a rider on the Wall of Death, there was a chance it would fall gradually to the bottom and stay there, and then you won a prize. This happened twice for me. I won two metal badges, each about an inch across and coloured bright blue. They were singularly worthless in the terms in which the world accounts worth, but how do you reckon true worth for a boy who normally never won anything but was now treading on air as he wore the badges proudly one on each side of his jersey?

I remember the other incident because it was epoch-making. At the edge of the fair, away from the babble of the crowd, was a mysterious enclosed booth. At first nobody went nigh nor by it, so that one felt the owner must be sunk deep below the breadline – times were hard in 1923, harder than we can conceive of today. But as the afternoon wore on a miracle happened. A queue to the booth began to form, growing ever longer as time passed by. At last my father could restrain his curiosity no longer, and even though he ascertained the cost of entrance to be no less than sixpence he stuck it out in the queue until his turn came. Reader, do not think this was a topless affair or some other pornography that was being offered. Such things were not permitted in my youth. The best you could then manage were those seaside postcards, coloured in bright red, which offered jokes so thin as to be without the slightest interest to the sophisticated industrial population of my native district.

My father reeled, glassy-eyed, from the covered booth. 'They call it wireless,' he said. I regret my father did not cough up another sixpence for me to experience the miracle he had just witnessed. In retrospect, however, it was easily possible to reconstruct the situation, for pretty soon we had bundles of copper wire, cardboard tubes and bits of insulating ebonite all over the house; and in a dozen other houses in our little village there were similar scenes. These were the days in which low-power radio stations were springing up all over Britain, and there was intense competition among the villagers as to who could receive the call-signs of the most distant transmitters. Grown men would sit up late at night, hunched over their little crystal-rectifying receivers, listening with headphones for those whisper-faint call-signs.

Everybody knew about wavelengths, because each transmitting station had a different wavelength and you had to make up a different tuning coil for each one. This was why the houses were forever strewn with insulated copper wire. I tried my hand at winding coils, but at the age of eight I made such a mess of it, getting the wire into a tangle like an unruly ball of wool, that eventually both my parents baulked – my mother at the mess and my father at the cost of the wire I was rendering useless.

Perhaps it was because of my lack of success at winding coils that I turned my thoughts to the problem of what 'wavelength' meant, rather as I had done earlier with telling the time. But 'wavelength' was a much harder nut to crack, and somewhat naturally I had to drop it eventually. As things turned out, I didn't find myself in a position to understand the real meaning of a radio wavelength until I was approaching twenty, so the solution to this problem had a long wait – though not so long as others were to take in later life. Although I was immediately disappointed in this particular regard, perhaps the sight of all those coils and of the huge span of wire – the aerial – running from the house to the very top of a tall, neighbouring tree influenced me to find out eventually what it all meant.

I began this chapter by comparing the world as youngsters see it today with the world as we saw it. Our world would have seemed incredibly mean to a modern child, mean with hovels, with cheap leaky shoes, with undernourishment, and without cars to ride in or television to watch. Yet to us it was a world of perpetual wonderment, a world of unicorns that might just perhaps turn into real beasts, a world in which there might even be a ghost around the next corner of a dark lane. What we actually found around the next corner, to our perpetual disappointment, was a couple hugging each other, which seemed the silliest possible waste of time.

A considerable fraction of my own time between five and ten was spent in the invention of games, as was that of all the boys around me. I do not recall ever being provided in those years with a game by adults – there were none at the schools I attended. We made everything up for ourselves. This was a piece of real luck, for I had caught the tail-end of one of the greatest periods in human history for the invention of games – football, rugby, cricket, tennis, golf, baseball, winter sports, almost every game you can think of had its ideas and rules developed in that period of which I saw the closing moments. By contrast, the inventiveness of the modern era is as near zero as makes no difference. Today it needs an international revolution to change the rules of football by even a short hair. So far as sport is concerned we do not live today in an inventive era. For other activities such as science the situation isn't quite so obvious, but it is a pertinent question whether the state of affairs in sport isn't typical of all society, science included. Science magazines and science programmes on radio and television maintain strenuously that it is otherwise, of course, but most of the stuff one hears has to be taken with a pinch of salt. It is expensive gloss, just as new-style boots and rackets and golf-clubs are only glossy details which tend to conceal the fact that nothing fundamental is happening within the games themselves. I rather suspect that historians of the future will see our present age as one of low inventiveness all round, to be explained as a combination of too much affluence and of the ubiquitousness of communications and media pressure.

Chapter Three

A CHILD SOON learns it has a special relationship with its mother, and with its father a little while later, but it is not until the age of about three that the child perceives a similar relationship for others. Then it does so mostly for children whom it meets and plays with, who can also be seen to have mothers and fathers. Grandparents are quite a problem to fit into place, especially as there may be two sets of them. The concept that one's own parents also have parents is an awkward one. In my own case this critical aspect of life was made still more awkward by the fact that, while both my grandmothers lived close by in Gilstead, neither of my grandfathers was still alive, so there were no obvious pairings to be spotted. George Hoyle, my paternal grandfather, came from Rochdale in Lancashire. Like so many menfolk in the district he earned his living in the textile business, but his real interests, according to older relatives who knew him, were in mathematics and chess.

I was never able in my youth to sort out the larger family relationships which, from listening to my parents, I realised I possessed. My paternal grandparents had both been married before, so as well as my own direct line there were children from two sets of former marriages. I had great grandparents with a family of thirteen, some lines of which had proliferated further. The details seemed too amazing to be true. I was somehow related to the Hammond family of Bradford, which owned Hammond's Brewery and counted itself among the plutocracy of the district. I do not recall seeing a Hammond, although every day in my teens I passed billboards on my way to school which bore big posters that read 'Hammond Ales', displaying a hefty fellow drinking from a large tankard, posters which were plastered throughout the Bradford area. I would pause in front of one of them to search my empty jacket in the hope that a coin might have slipped through a hole into the inner lining, and would think to myself how fine it must be to own a brewery. The Hammonds were elusive people. I learned in later life that they had sent their carriage to my great grandfather's funeral, but didn't attend themselves, despite the relationship and despite his being regarded as one of the outstanding Yorkshire poets of his day.

Better known to me was my Uncle Harry, actually my Great Uncle Harry, who visited my parents from time to time. I always liked Great Uncle Harry, even though he dressed in rags. The rags seemed less important to me than his invariably complimentary remark: 'Now *there's* a grand lad.' On one of his visits my mother was having trouble in shutting a warped door. Knowing Uncle Harry was supposed to have received training as a joiner my mother permitted him to fix it, which he rapidly did by slicing away at the door with an axe, much to my father's grief when he came home in the evening. Like me, Uncle Harry didn't have two penny pieces to rub together, because if he was ever so fortunate he immediately made his way at the double to the nearest pub. A time came when the family decided Uncle Harry's rags were not helpful to its own social standing. So they fitted him out with a resplendent new suit, only for the suit to disappear within the week, doubtless into the hands of a pawnbroker. To the family's frenzied demand to know what had happened to the suit, Uncle Harry declared that it had blown away in a strong wind on Saltaire Bridge, and from this view of what had transpired he could not be budged; the seeds of imaginative greatness must have lain tragically dormant in my Great Uncle Harry.

Then there was Black Uncle Jack, actually my Great Uncle Jack, who my father always insisted was much the strongest man in the district. I never saw Uncle Jack, but stories of his prowess lit up my young life as the night-time tipping of molten iron from a furnace lights up the clouds overhead. After a day's work, Black Uncle Jack would become blind drunk. He was not welcome in the local pubs because in such situations he would flay alive anybody who should contradict him in the smallest degree. The nearest character I have come on in world literature to my Great Uncle Jack was Brandy Bottle Bates in the stories of Damon Runyon. There was, I believe, general relief in the district when one dark night, following just such a combative evening, my Great Uncle Jack fell on his way home into the local canal, and became 'drowned dead', as Charles Dickens' Mr Peggotty would have said. This was the Leeds-to-Liverpool canal, the 'cut' as it was known in the local vernacular.

There is no way a person could judge today from visiting a modern pub how beer drinking used to be in the good old days. There was a middle-aged man in my village, not a relative this time, of whom most drinkers stood in some awe. He heard one evening of a pub some four miles away which was opening that very evening under new management and in the interests of goodwill was dispensing free beer. With a thunderous cry of, 'Why didn't anybody tell'm?' he raced out of the village and downhill pell-mell into the town of Bingley, where he set off, still in full cry, in the direction of Cross-flatts. He was said to have reached the pub at half past nine. Half an hour later, at the statutory closing time of ten o'clock, he rolled out of the pub into the street, ten pints of beer to the good – or to the bad, as the temperance folk saw it.

Life was so closed in by what we would regard today as severe poverty and by a lack of communications – closed in except for the local cinema for which one paid 1*d* or 0.4p to gain entrance into what was popularly known as the 'bug hole' – that a large majority of the menfolk spent their evenings in the pubs. Beer in those days was priced at only a penny or two to the pint; at such low cost, drinking was necessarily excessive, and the tendency was for the male population to be formed into two disparate groups – either you drank to excess or you didn't drink at all. I do not recall a commercially produced alcoholic beverage ever being brought into our house. This wasn't because my parents were doctrinaire about alcohol the way some people were, but because they saw it as an all or nothing situation.

A Mr Bartle came to live in our village. He was an extreme temperance advocate. Between the ages of eight and twelve I saw quite a bit of Mr Bartle, a man with a cherry-red nose, because his house was close by, and partly because in co-operation with the local church he made temperance propaganda among us young fry. The organisation in question was called the Band of Hope, a title more frank in its honesty than most. The main consideration was that if we joined the Band of Hope we obtained the use of a large warm church hut in winter on a particular night of the week, Tuesday I think. There were clear bribes from time to time of buns and cakes, consumed with much speed and relish. Also from time to time there were harangues from visiting personages, which even in my tender years I couldn't help viewing with a certain morbid fascination. A singer in a stiff collar stands out sharply in my memory, a singer who rendered the toreador's song from *Carmen* accompanied by piano and trumpet, an occasion not to be missed. More routinely, we would be shown lantern slides of drops of water and alcohol, the water teeming with ugly-looking creatures, the alcohol devoid of such things. 'There,' the lecturer would say, 'nothing can live in alcohol,' whereon Mr Bartle would intone in a sombre voice, 'Never let a drop of it pass your lips.' Meanwhile some of us would have realised there were other very different interpretations of what we had just seen.

When I was eleven or so, Mr Bartle persuaded me to enter the annual Band of Hope examination, the syllabus for which in that particular year included an extensive section dealing with the brewing of alcoholic beverages. Whether somebody had thought it a joke, or clergymen were themselves looking for instruction in the art of home brewing, I don't know, but astonishingly there it was, and since by now I had become keenly interested in chemistry the examination seemed like money for old rope. More precisely, the first prize was £10 in book-tokens. My itch to instruct the clergy in the practice of home brewing was such that I did indeed win first prize, not only for the Dioceses of Ripon and Bradford but even nationally, a meteoric situation indeed for our little village. I had to journey to the City of Bradford to receive my prize and to be patted on the head by the Bishop. I would have preferred it if I had been patted by the winner of the second prize, a good-looking farmer's daughter from Gargrave in the upper Aire Valley. Gargrave was twenty-five miles from Bingley, so it seemed impossible I would ever see the girl again, and I didn't.

Drinking fermented fruit wines was thought to be in order by all but the more rigorous teetotallers, although with poorly controlled fermentation such as then was practised fruit wines must have contained esters and higher alcohols which really are damaging to the human body. The whizz woman at making fruit wines in my village was my maternal grandmother, Mary Ellen

Preston, known familiarly as Polly. In my time, Polly was a white-haired, good-looking woman in her sixties, the terror of the district, although to me she was never anything but my kind old grandmother. People said I was like her, and in a stubborn obstinacy to get ourselves into trouble this seems to have been true. In recent years my wife asked a hundred-year-old relative what Polly was like in her youth. The old lady got as far as 'What was Polly like ...' and then broke into a cackle of laughter, after which we couldn't get a further word out of her, so shocking apparently had been the situation.

I was vaguely aware that my mother's sister, my Aunt Leila (girls in those days still suffered from Byronic names), was somehow different. She was tall, always beautifully dressed in clothes she made herself, and she took me from time to time to Lingard's shop in Bradford, where she bought ice cream and I was able to watch the amazing mechanics of containers which shop assistants kept shooting along wires to a central cash desk. In the early years of the century, Aunt Leila had earned money from sewing to help my mother with her musical training in London. What was different about Aunt Leila was that she was illegitimate. I have never learned who the father was, so all I can say is that unless he died or Polly had given him his marching orders, he was a fool not to have claimed such a daughter.

It is impossible today to understand the intensity of the stigma of illegitimacy as it existed in the late nineteenth century, and as it existed even in the nineteen-twenties during my boyhood. This situation for Polly must have been made worse by the peculiar Yorkshire illusion that by rubbing hard enough on a wound it will somehow be healed. If a man struggled ill to work he would be greeted by, 'Ee, lad, th'art not looking thizen, art tha?' Or to a girl sensitive about a little adolescent acne, 'Ee, lass, th'art real spotty, arn't tha?' Bernard Miles once told me a story, due I think to Harry Secombe, who had finished a turn at the Alhambra Theatre in Bradford, leaving his audience rolling in the aisles. On Secombe's way out of the theatre, a stage hand called after him: 'Ee, 'arry lad, tha a'most made mi laugh.' Bernard Miles also told me, unaware that I was Ben Preston's great grandson, that Preston was one of the three surviving poets in the Yorkshire dialect. Unfortunately, the real dialect is hard to understand today, even for Yorkshire people. The real dialect was already pretty attenuated in my boyhood, and now a half-century later it is essentially gone.

Ben Preston conveyed the popular excitement about railways in a racy jingle he wrote for a Bradford newspaper on the occasion of the opening of the railway through the Aire Valley. From our present-day, technologically sophisticated standpoint it is hardly possible to appreciate the emotional impact of the railway as it appeared to those who actually witnessed it. An important aspect, easily overlooked, was that an age-old class structure based on the horse was largely destroyed, a class structure whose remnants we still see today in the Enclosure at Ascot. The aristocracy and plutocracy had their own horses and carriages, while by clubbing together the middle class gave financial support to the stage-coach system. Poorer folk walked. With the coming of the railway all this was changed in a moment. Anyone with a few pence could suddenly travel faster and farther than any aristocrat on his horse. If we take literally the ebullience of Ben Preston's poem *The Locomotive*, we come close to a sense of how things must really have felt to those who experienced the historic coming of the railway:

> The neigh of the dragon, a terrible cry,
> Wild, piercing, and shrill, has gone up to the sky;
> He pants for the start, and he snorts in his ire,
> His life-blood is boiling, his heart is on fire.
>
> O man, O my brother, how stubborn thy will,

How dauntless thy courage, how Godlike thy skill:
The Earth, with its elements, yields to the brave,
The fire is a bondsman, the vapour a slave,
The vales are uplifted, the mountains are riven,
And the way of the dragon is shining and even.
Let us gaze and admire, and declare, if we can,
How mighty the God that created the man.

From Ben Preston's other writings it is clear that 'the man' was not used generically, but was an explicit reference to George Stephenson, whom he greatly admired.

Ironically, Ben's best-known bit of writing, the hymn *Onward Christian Soldiers*, is not attributed to him at all. At least Ben's younger daughters, who were alive in my time, were always emphatic about his authorship of the hymn, and the actual words themselves together with the circumstances in which they were written would seem to bear the family out. The time was around 1864, and the occasion the annual Easter parade of schoolchildren in Bradford, who by tradition carried a large number of banners. There really was a 'royal banner' and there really was a 'cross of Jesus' carried at the head of the parade. S. Baring Gould, to whom the hymn is usually attributed, was, as I understand it, a young clergyman newly arrived in the Bradford district who wanted a special hymn to celebrate the occasion. Hearing of Ben Preston's reputation as a poet, Baring Gould asked my great grandfather for words appropriate to the circumstances of the parade. No attribution was given at the time because by 1864 Ben Preston had changed from the early pro-religious stance of *The Locomotive*, perhaps under the influence of Charles Darwin's book *On the Origin of Species,* which appeared in 1859. Ben Preston was also at the time turning from being a liberal writer to becoming a socialist one. Eventually the hymn was attributed to Baring Gould by default.

The notion that things are frequently not the way they

are supposed to be entered my head at an early age, a favourable situation for a prospective scientist. Catholics were anathema in our district. The local Catholic school was cleverly placed so that its pupils were unlikely to encounter lads of the much more numerous Protestant population. Even so, the Protestant youth would occasionally converge with evil intent on the Catholic school, stoning the Catholic pupils in true biblical fashion as they emerged into a veritable hellbrew, scattering them shrieking in all directions like birds under a hawk. I took no part in these activities because two of my best friends in the village were Catholics, a boy of about my own age and an older girl who was good at organising games. They were outsiders who stayed only for a few years.

Then there were the Jews, a considerable number of whom had settled in and around the City of Leeds, having escaped from persecutions in Poland and the Ukraine. They set up as tailors, often enough, which brought some of them into a business connection with my father. We had no such words in our local speech as 'cheat' or 'swindle'. The standard local expression if you were cheated was to say you'd been 'jewed'. I used the word many times myself before its connotation occurred to me, but I ceased to use it after the following little episode, which requires an introduction describing my father's business, and indeed the general business practices at the time in the City of Bradford.

Bradford was then a world leader in the weaving of high-quality cloth. It exported its products internationally, as well as supplying Bond Street tailors in London. Occasionally looms would go slightly wrong and would turn out cloth with some very minor flaw, which only the eye of an expert could detect. Such high-grade 'seconds' were sold off at small fractions of the price of flawless cloth. My father was friendly with the foremen and managers of many of the Bradford mills, and so was privy to where seconds were to be obtained. His business was to build a stock of seconds, which he then passed on to a wide range of customers, exporting the cloth to places as far away as China, and selling it to the Jewish tailors from Leeds.

Payments for 'deals' were always made, as far as I could see, by cheque. As soon as a purchaser handed his cheque to a vendor, the vendor would immediately 'ship' the goods. Shipping the goods consisted of calling in one of the flat horse-drawn carts that hired themselves out almost like taxis. Any day you went into Bradford during business hours you would see a score of these flat carts rattling along cobbled streets. The whole centre of Bradford was a mass of horse dung, and in winter you could detect a dozen piles of the stuff smoking in the cool air.

The morality of cashing cheques was a little curious. If a vendor went immediately to the purchaser's bank and the cheque bounced, this was distinctly bad form. But if the vendor permitted more than an understood length of time to elapse before he presented the cheque, the more fool he if it bounced. Friday afternoon was the usual deadline for settling deals.

On the occasion in question, my father had forgotten by Friday afternoon to cash a cheque he'd received from a Jewish tailor, presumably due to the pressure of other business. Over and over through the following weekend my mother and I had to agonise over my father's frenzied cries that he would be 'jewed'. Since the sum was of an order that seemed considerable in those days, we were naturally appalled at the situation – I was about ten at the time, just the sort of age to be appalled. My father went off to business as usual on the Monday morning, returning as usual in the afternoon at about five o'clock. My mother gave him a cup of tea and then waited with mounting impatience as he drank it. 'Well, Ben?' she said, unable to contain herself any longer. 'He paid,' said my father at last and then added, as if to defend the local prejudice: 'But they tell me he's religious.' These were the seeds that, flowering in later life, have caused me to entertain reservations about everything I hear, unless it is based either on observed facts or on mathematical calculations.

The first person known to me with whom I have genes in common was a certain John Preston, who in the late eighteenth century amassed a fortune through dealing in wool, owning at one time a considerable fraction of the property in central Bradford. John Preston had the enviable gift of selling at the top of the market, declaring, 'Ah'll sell, even if ah repent it.' He became such a byword for this tactic that his fame even crossed the Atlantic. A cartoon sketch of him is said to have hung for many years at the entrance to the Merchant's Club in New York.

John Preston had no children but he had a favourite nephew, William Preston, who was directly in my own ancestral line. William Preston was given a good schooling at John's expense, and all seemed set fair for my ancestral line. I might thus have been born with a silver spoon in my mouth, as my father was fond of remarking about the well-to-do. But unfortunately John Preston did what other rich and clever businessmen have been known to do. Doubtless imagining he would never die at all, John Preston died intestate, a dreaded word in our family. A sister or sisters of John Preston won his riches, and young William Preston was left to sample life in a woolsorter's job in a Bradford mill.

William Preston still had one shot left in his locker. He was educated in a day when educated young men in Bradford were not to be found on every tree. With this shot he won the affections of Anne Hammond from the wealthy Hammond family. For marrying below her station Anne Hammond appears to have been cut off with the proverbial shilling. The shilling sufficed, however, to educate her two sons, Ben and John Preston, the one becoming the poet and the other an artist. Ben Preston escaped from the woolsorters' shed at the age of eighteen by writing a political poem which was said to have won a local parliamentary election for the Liberal candidate, the poem being a lampoon on the Tories. Thereafter, Ben eked out a somewhat precarious existence as a poet, as a journalist with the local Bradford paper, and by poetry readings from Shakespeare and Milton – industrial England was first becoming literate at this time – which sometimes took place in St George's Hall in Bradford, where my mother would perform professionally as a singer two generations later. Both for Ben Preston and his younger brother John, the Hammond connection ultimately became of dominant importance through the sustained generosity of 'Uncle' Ben Hammond.

Like old John Preston, 'Uncle' Ben Hammond was a dealer, but in cattle rather than wool. Like old John Preston he amassed a huge fortune, and like old John Preston he had no children. Unlike old John Preston, however, he did not hang on to his money to die intestate. He discovered a truth first expounded with great clarity by the French writer François Rabelais. Hang on to your money, said Rabelais, and all your family and acquaintances will gather round like vultures waiting for you to die. But amass huge debts and your creditors will be most solicitous of your health, sending you the best possible doctors in the hope of your surviving to square accounts. 'Uncle' Ben Hammond didn't run himself into debt, quite the reverse, but he gave away most of his fortune to his thirty-odd nephews and nieces several years before his death. On one occasion, at a dinner held in 1882 in a Bradford hotel, he gave away some £30,000 in a single evening, which was a lot of money in those distant, pre-inflation days.

None of 'Uncle' Ben Hammond's money ever came my way, however. Because of Ben Preston's thirteen children, his share of the spoils was inevitably thinned down, and what remained mostly went to Ben's younger daughters, who looked after him in his old age. This was seen as fair enough by the family, but when the youngest daughter then married and willed the money partially into her husband's family, harsh things were said that delighted my young ears.

In the longer run, young John Preston's family did better because young John Preston had only one child – a son who married a Cornish woman, thus breaking out of the local pattern of inbreeding. The result was a considerable family in the second generation with vigorous, good-looking and long-lived children. The men lived to their eighties and nineties and two of the women to over a hundred – I referred to one of them earlier in connection with my grandmother Polly. Young John Preston would have applauded the friend of Franz Schubert's family who, when asked the name of Franz' teacher, replied: 'What need of a teacher has a boy who learned his music from God?' The notion that natural ability is best left to assert itself without technical training continued in John Preston's line until my own generation, which was unfortunate because his granddaughter Nannie had a genuine gift for draughtsmanship. Nannie was a cuddly-looking woman who would come to our house and draw for me anything I cared to name – horses, rabbits and so on – all done in a flash. Nannie did the first colour brochure for the original Marks, the founder of the Marks & Spencer empire. True to young John Preston's mystic philosophy, one of his descendants recently gave Nannie's originals to the memorabilia of the Marks & Spencer empire, for nothing. Old John Preston, 'Sell-and-Repent Preston' as he was generally known, would not have approved of such munificence.

How it came about that our side of the family had no truck with the 'genius will out' philosophy, I don't know. My mother had already made her views clear when, against all the odds, she made her way to London in order to receive a technical training at the Royal Academy of Music. There was never any thought in our household but that I must receive as severe a technical training as possible – in something, although exactly in what remained to be decided. How things eventually worked out I will relate in later chapters.

But all this is really rather petty stuff, as is every family tree I ever saw. Mankind has not changed much since the days of Cro-Magnon man, days separated from our own times by a thousand generations. Every one of us has an immense line filled with stories of struggle, heroism, self-sacrifice, that if we did but know it would put the parochial affairs of the past few generations to shame. Every one of us has an immense line that would sweep even the greatest dynasties of recorded history into affairs of minor consequence. And before Cro-Magnon there were upwards of ten thousand generations, so many that the imagination is too staggered to conceive of what happened to them all on a generation-to-generation basis. What we actually see are nothing but bits of foam at the surface of the vast ocean of prehistory.

CHAPTER FOUR

I COULD WRITE out the multiplication tables up to $12 \times 12 = 144$ at the age of four, but I couldn't really read until I was seven. I can remember precisely when I first learned to read properly. It was in the 'bug hole' of the local cinema. Those were the days of silent films with subtitles. To my surprise, I found I was suddenly reading the subtitles without difficulty. Within a week or two I was reading generally. Rather obviously I had suffered from an eye-focus problem.

In my late teens I was destined to suffer from severe headaches. After a remission of forty years the headaches returned, fortunately only briefly. On the recent occasion I made an effort to discover what the trouble was. A highly competent general practitioner, an eye-specialist, and a neurologist made the same diagnosis, migraine: 'Ah ha! You are an absolutely classic example of migraine,' they all said with satisfaction. Since every one of them then went on to say that nobody really understands the cause of migraine, this was actually no diagnosis at all. My own suggestion, applicable to my case at least, of an eye-focus problem did not win much support, but this remains my opinion. Migraine is a clinical condition which can have many sources, and eye-focus problems may be one of them. It was mainly important to me at the age of nineteen because I had a literally blinding migraine during the last paper of one of the most important examinations of my life.

Between the ages of five and nine I was almost perpetually at war with the educational system. The devices by which I whittled down what should normally have been four years of schooling into only one year will form the topic of this chapter. My father always deferred to my mother's judgement in the several crises of my early educational career, because she had been a schoolteacher herself, whereas he had been obliged for financial reasons to leave school for the mill at the age of eleven. The bare recital of events would suggest that my mother was unreasonably tolerant of my obduracy. But precisely because she had been a teacher herself, my mother could see that I made the best steps when I was left alone. I had learned to tell the time and I had fixed the multiplication tables imperishably in my mind alone; in addition, circumstances in which I learned to read in the bug hole of the local cinema – all in a flash and shortly to be recounted in detail – were sufficient to bemuse any sensitive parent.

Yet my mother knew with the certainty that night follows day that without formal schooling I would never hoist myself onto the scholarship ladder which could take me first to the local grammar school, and then to university. Her problem, therefore, was to persuade me to submit to the necessary degree of formal teaching without the streak of originality being knocked out of me by the use of force. It was due to her forbearance, and to her realisation at the biggest crisis point that I was factually correct while the school system was wrong, that things eventually worked out as she and my father had hoped.

The elementary educational system began normally at five, and from five to six you were an infant. In each succeeding year you passed from one 'standard' to another, ending at the age of fourteen in Standard VIII. The infant year was not obligatory by law, so that children were not actually forced into school until the age of six. As soon as I learned from my mother that there was a place called school which I must attend willy nilly – a place where you were obliged to think about matters prescribed by a 'teacher', not about matters decided by yourself – I was appalled. Since I made it abundantly clear that I would not accept incarceration in a mental prison house, my mother began by permitting me to ditch the first infant year, in which nothing of substance was taught anyway. But when my sixth birthday arrived on 24 June 1921, the nettle had at last to be grasped. The solution which appeared to present itself was the following.

In 1920 there was a temporary trade boom, with my father's business in Bradford doing well for a while, which made it possible for me to begin school in July 1921 at a small private establishment located not far from the mill where Damart clothing is manufactured today. This particular school was chosen because the children of my mother's contemporaries on young John Preston's side of the family had been sent there. The tactic worked in the short term, which is to say through the month of July 1921. After that, freakish factors intervened.

Following the trade boom of 1920 the cloth trade fell on hard times in 1921, making it more likely that my father would lose money rather than gain it if he continued in business. So, with my mother ill following the birth of my sister, it was decided at the end of July 1921 that we would all go as paying guests to the house of a man in Essex known to my father because he'd been secretary to Keir Hardie, the first Labour Member of Parliament. The Essex countryside to which we retreated in the environs of the town of Rayleigh was quite rural in those days. During August 1921 I had a companion of about my own age, Freddie Clamp, who knew a thing or two about devilment that had never occurred to the village boys of Gilstead. The time came in September when I was required, together with Freddie Clamp, to cross a common, which I recall in distant memory as being bright with gorse bushes, in order to attend school in the nearby village of Thundersley. It was during September and October 1921 that Freddie Clamp and I worked out a system of truancy which supplied the essential basis of the technique I was to use in succeeding years. Freddie Clamp's father was at sea, an officer in the navy, and it was then that I acquired a mystical respect for the Royal Navy which I have never since been able to shake off.

It had been my father's intention to stay in Essex until the business climate improved, but by October there were disturbing intelligences from my maternal grandmother, the redoubtable Polly, which brought us all hot-foot back to Gilstead in November. To my father's chagrin, we found that the man called Brady to whom the house had been rented had done a flit. The word 'flit' was in widespread use in those days. Nobody thought of it as the past tense of the verb 'to fly'. It meant running up debts and then getting out fast, before creditors got clued up on the situation, as Americans say.

Our house must have been below the standard to which Brady and his family were accustomed. But it had a grand-sounding name, 4, Milnerfield Villas, which was presumably what really counted in their scheme of things. Brady made the mistake of running up huge grocery bills in my father's name, otherwise he could have got away with the deception for several months more. Like all successful entrepreneurs, Brady had flair. He entered his younger children at the local grammar school and then had their school uniforms made specially to measure, instead of accepting them off the peg as you or I would have done. After all, if you have no intention of paying, why not have the best? He hired a Rolls-Royce car and chauffeur. His older daughter, whom I remember as being exceedingly good-looking, drove in the Rolls to Bradford where she cleaned out the best dress shops of their most expensive creations. All this uproar was milk and honey to me, of course, and it occupied the time very handily until the question of school again raised its head at the beginning of January 1922. I returned to the same private school as before, but I returned no longer an innocent child prepared to have irrelevant knowledge poured into my head by the old beldame who ran the place. Thanks to the Royal Navy – at one stage removed – it was an experienced young blackguard who entered the same school one morning in early January 1922.

The situation as it now presented itself to my mind was that you spent the first bit of the morning from nine to ten getting interested in something. Then, just as you were nicely into your stride, there was a jump to something else. Once again you co-operated with the teacher by becoming interested in the new topic. But all to no avail. Like somebody with St Vitus's Dance, the teacher was off again into a new subject which bore not the slightest resemblance to anything that had gone before. The thing which eventually finished that first school for me was connected, as you might expect, with numbers. Because I found the sums I was given rather easy, I was told to learn the Roman numeral system, whereby I found to my amazement that VIII stood for simple old 8. How could anybody be so daft as to write VIII for 8, I wondered. Yet I made no instant complaint, for the task was not an onerous one. Besides, I hit a problem with some puzzlement in it – how did you multiply these strange new numbers? When the question proved intractable, I asked the teacher, only to be told that you didn't multiply Roman numbers. When I persisted by asking what were they good for then, the answer was that Roman numbers were very old and that they were sometimes used in books.

This was more than I could reasonably stomach, and the day this outrage to the intelligence was perpetrated became my last at that particular school. The date must have been early March. Using the avoidance tactics Freddie Clamp and I had worked out, I contrived to persuade my parents that I was in attendance at school, and through the agency of a friendly boy in the village I conveyed to the school the sad news that I was confined at home with a ghastly illness. Amazingly, the bubble lasted until late April or early May, and it only burst because a contemporary of my mother's with children at the school, hearing I was at death's door, expressed concern about it. As fate would have it, I found myself with the trump cards in the row which followed, because it was during this spasm of truancy that I learned to read while patronising the bug hole in the Hippodrome cinema. To this point my parents had awarded the old lady at the school the credit for teaching me to read. Now they were nonplussed to see that this was not so. Ever one to press a solid argument, I emphasised that if I'd continued at school I would *never* have learned to read. The bug hole at the Hippodrome was evidently a superior educational establishment, I persisted, and at 1*d* per admission, a good deal cheaper than school. Whatever way you looked at it, the case was unanswerable.

My parents had no recourse but to explain the law governing attendance at school, which at least set an interesting problem worth thinking about. How was it, I wondered, that the law could pursue so relentlessly a harmless boy like me while permitting Brady and his family to do a flit with all those debts unpaid? After worrying at this problem like a dog with a bone I concluded that unhappily I'd been born into a world dominated by a rampaging monster called 'law', that was both all-powerful and all-stupid, a view which has resurfaced from time to time ever since.

The outcome was a compromise. To avoid the family being punitively fined and us all ending up in the workhouse, I would yield myself up to the enemy, but not until the beginning of the next school year in early September. Since I would pass the age of seven on 24 June, I had therefore defeated the educational system at this point by essentially two whole years. My parents permitted me to choose the next school to 'come to the mound', as one says in baseball terminology. I opted for a state elementary school in Bingley, largely because several of my mates in the village went there. It was a good joke to start with that the headmaster's name was Woodcock; he was a walrus-moustached man who always wore a stiff collar. Nobody in the Aire Valley, except I suppose a refined one percent, used any other word for penis except 'cock'. So here was a ha-ha situation from the outset. In addition to this, Woodcock in his daily morning ramble to the school persistently referred to the local Bradford newspaper, which everybody knew to be the *Observer* in the morning and the *Daily Telegraph* in the evening, as the *Argus*, which everybody also knew meant 'arse'. But although the situation was daft enough, it was at least an improvement on Roman numerals.

State schools were all mixed. There were two spells each of fifteen minutes, one in the morning, the other in the afternoon, when the children were put out into so-called 'playgrounds'. Playgrounds were rigorously separated between boys and girls by a high wall. At no time do I recall any effort being made by the boys to invade the girls' playground. Since no teacher was ever there to monitor the state of play, it is clear that a strict taboo must have become established early in the school system, presumably by frequent canings and the like. Growing up later with the taboo, we simply accepted it.

At Mornington Road School the boys went in

through big iron gates on a street close by a large Methodist church. The gates led into the boys' playground. There were specially grand stone flags leading immediately to the school, but over the rest of the playground the surface was in need of repair. At all events, the playground was hard-surfaced, so that heavy boots running on it were very audible. There was a big slow-witted lad who was approaching the school-leaving age of fourteen. Because of his slow wits he was the unfortunate butt of his class. The standard practice at playtime was for him to chase after his contemporaries in studded boots, aiming kicks wildly in all directions, to immense roars of laughter from the others. The day came when this lad acquired a horsewhip with which he was able to make immense cracking noises in the chase. My memory is that the thing went on for weeks, with every play period shrill with shouts of laughter. I swear that at no time did any teacher intervene. For small fry like me at the bottom of the school, it was actually easy to keep well out of the way, and again I swear that I found the situation a great deal more entertaining than Roman numerals.

Although I had as yet received no formal education to speak of, because I could read now and knew about numbers I was put into Standard II, the normal standard for my age. The examination-like tests which even quite young children were frequently given in those days were new to me, and in the first test or two I performed indifferently. But once I had the hang of what the tests were about I moved upwards in the class and was rewarded by a desk among the top echelon. On one occasion 'Argus' Woodcock even commended my example to the whole school, so that for a while it seemed as if at last I was set fair, particularly as the teacher, Sally Pearson, was both competent and pleasant.

I cannot explain why in looking through some old photographs recently I found a picture of my class taken towards the end of my first year at Mornington Road School the most poignant. Quite unlike the phantom recollections of my earliest years, the faces of my fellow pupils are etched in memory with total clarity. Locked in a time capsule in my brain, every one of the children in the picture is a Peter Pan who can never grow old, the rough diamond at the upper right of the picture and the gentlest boy in the class crouching at the lower left. There was not a pampered one among them. If you look carefully you can see the strains of malnutrition on some of the faces. Sadly, I can scarcely remember any of their names.

The real lives of my schoolfellows must now be spent, or nearly spent. I can only hope fate dealt kindly with them, although I know that in at least one case it did not. Ours was but one class in one school in one small town, but standing there is a boy who became a member of Winston Churchill's select 'few', a fighter pilot who died in 1942 after receiving the Distinguished Flying Medal. Jim Hopewell was not the biggest or strongest boy in the class, but he was always the most active and best co-ordinated.

My days at Mornington Road School were already numbered by the time this photograph was taken, and I had already begun to suspect this would be so. The teacher in the next class upwards into which I would be passing was of the strong-armed variety. The woman's class was notorious as a regular charnel house of canings and beatings that would seem unbelievable today.

It needed little in the way of common sense to see, once I had moved into Standard III in September 1923 at the age of eight and had observed the first canings, that I would need to spend the coming year not in learning but in self-preservation, and indeed I managed to get through to the spring of 1924 with only a few weeks' attendance at school. By now I had learned that illness was the key to absence. Doubtless I experienced some genuine illnesses during the winter of 1923-4, but additionally I spun out every small sniffle into a week or ten days. The tactic led to frequent examinations by Dr Crocker, who found it difficult to diagnose malingering since I had never malingered before. Eventually Dr Crocker diagnosed tonsils and adenoids and recommended their removal, which minor operation and subsequent convalescence I stretched to two months. Eventually, the sniffles disappeared with the coming of warmer weather in the spring of 1924, so unfortunately I ran out of further excuses and had perforce to return to school. By now, however, I could see light at the end of the tunnel. A few months more and I would be gone from the universally dreaded Standard III into Standard IV, which was reputed to be much better. With my eyes ever wide open for trouble, I thought I might avoid it. Then, just as I was picking up a little confidence, disaster struck in a way I had failed to anticipate.

The spring flowers were in bloom now, and we were asked to collect a specified list of about twenty kinds. Because I lived out of the town and had roamed the countryside since the age of five, I knew exactly where the flowers could be found. It was no great trouble, therefore, for me to collect the whole list, and thinking to ingratiate myself with the dreaded teacher, I did so. Therein was my error – for when the teacher gave a lesson on the flowers, I was able to compare what she said with the specimens in my hand. One particular flower was said to have five petals. Mine had six. Here was a bit of a problem, I thought. If my flower had been a petal short I could have understood that it might somehow have lost one. But how could my flower have a petal extra? Or could it be that this abominable teacher didn't know the difference between five and six? I had reached this point in my thinking when I received a stinging blow on the side of the head and a strident voice ordered me to pay attention.

The blow was delivered flat-handed across the ear. Since the teacher was certainly right-handed, the blow must therefore have been across my left ear, the one in which I was to become deaf in later life. Since, moreover, I wasn't expecting it at all I had no opportunity to flinch by the half-inch or so that would have reduced the impulsive pressure on my drum and middle ear. Joseph Conrad wrote a novel concerned with an underground political movement in East Europe before the Russian Revolution of 1917. A man suspected of being a police informer is tried and found guilty by a secret court. He is then held by two men while a third hits him a flat-handed blow first across one ear and then across the other, after which he is released. As he emerges from the cellar in which he has been tried into the street above, he realises to his horror that he is totally deaf. The story has the chilling quality which comes, I would suppose, from being based on a real event. Although it may seem fanciful, these several factors have caused me to wonder if the blow I thus received might not have had something to do with the later deafness. Perhaps, perhaps not.

As I recovered from the immediate pain of the blow, it became apparent that a total crisis in my relations with the educational system had at last been reached. Cost what it might in the way of the law, of fines, of the workhouse for my parents, I was done with it. First, I pocketed the flower with its six petals. Then I put up my hand and asked to go 'out', which meant going to the bogs – 'toilets' or 'lavatories' would have been quite misleading words because they were neither, they were bogs, in the good old-fashioned sense. Such a request was never refused, for obvious reasons. When I emerged from the school building into the boys' playground, instead of heading up the playground and slightly to the right, which was the way to the bogs, I kept straight ahead along the grand flagged path which led to the main iron gates, and thence into the sidestreet beside the big Methodist church. Half an hour later I was home, with the news for my mother that, come hell or high water, I was finished with school.

My mother must by now have suspected something was going badly wrong at the school, and as she heard my story and examined the flower herself she could see at last what it was. Like most adults, however, her thoughts were on some form of honourable compromise. I was never one for compromise myself, and since politics is said to be the art of compromise I was never one for politics either. Pretty soon I was back at Mornington Road School, not in Standard III, however, but in 'Argus' Woodcock's office with my mother, who to my delight was in one of her rare angry moods. But not to my delight at all, 'Argus' and my mother were evidently moving to patch up the situation, a promise being offered that there would be no further assaults provided I returned forthwith to the school. No deal, I told my mother afterwards, no way. To the question of what I would do if I didn't go to school, I replied that there were plenty of things to do. After all, I pointed out, I'd given the school system a try-out over three years, and if you didn't know something was no good after three years, what did you know?

Two or three weeks elapsed before my parents received a letter requesting that they present themselves at the offices of the local education committee. My father, being occupied with his business, left it to my mother to respond to the letter. She took me in tow, just as she had done on our visit to 'Argus' Woodcock. We were shown to an office where there were two men, one I think an education officer, the other probably a lawyer. The lawyer wore a big-winged collar which expanded and contracted like a spring as he moved about the office. After the legal position had been stated – it was an offence for parents not to *deliver* their children at school like sacks of merchandise – my mother tried to tell my story. At this I produced a tin box, opened it and took out the by now much faded flower. I asked the two gentlemen if they could count the number of petals. There are six, you see? And the teacher said there were five because she is unable to count up to six. I have no wish to go to schools where teachers can't count up to six, you see? And so on and on I went, grinding away on the theme of the teacher being unable to count up to six.

I suppose neither of the men knew that flowers which normally have five petals may have sports with six. They counted six for themselves, there were six plainly before their eyes, and with thirty children from my class as witnesses to the teacher saying five, the case was going to appear ludicrous if it ever came to court. My mother sensed that the day had been miraculously won. She pointed out her own qualifications as a schoolteacher, and we were permitted to leave with the understanding that nothing would be done, at least *pro tem.* As I retrieved the tin box with its flower I felt confident that the millstone of education had at last been lifted from my shoulders.

Each morning I ate breakfast and started off from home, just as if I were going to school. But it was to the factories and workshops of Bingley that I went. There were mills with clacking and thundering looms. There were blacksmiths and carpenters, but as yet no garages. The miraculous thing about it was that nobody told me to get out. Nobody boxed my ears or shouted that I must pay attention. Indeed, it was just the other way around. Everybody seemed amused to answer my questions.

The Leeds and Liverpool canal passes through Bingley. In those times there were many horse-drawn barges on the canal. A little north-west of the main town there are locks where the canal level changes. I spent many an hour watching in astonishment the simple ingenuity of the opening and closing of lock gates and sluices, and how marvellously the process effected the passage of the barges. Nobody had ever told me that these 'five-rise locks' were historically famous. In choosing them as a place worth spending many hours at, I like to think I was instinctively displaying a sound sense of engineering, and that the experience was of far more consequence than anything I might have been learning at school.

Indeed, the Bingley five-rise locks are still widely known and recently they were awarded first prize as the best-kept locks of the canal system. According to a nineteenth-century historian:

> The Leeds and Liverpool canal was opened 21st March 1774, when great rejoicing took place in Bingley. The church bells were rung, guns were fired by the local militia, and there was a general holiday. The first boat went down the five-rise locks in 28 minutes amid loud huzzas from the spectators. The locks here, as is well known, are unique on the Leeds and Liverpool system, and when they were completed were considered one of the grandest engineering achievements in the world.

My studies of the five-rise locks were always made in the mornings. Through the afternoons I made my way in the opposite direction, towards the moors, to explore in the woods and fields. It was then that I found the kingfisher's nest I mentioned in an earlier chapter. At the end of the afternoon I would return home for my tea, just as if I had been at school. Although I had no watch, there never seemed to be a problem in judging the time to within fifteen minutes or so.

Unfortunately I was not old enough yet to have a ticket for the Bingley public library. I suppose I could have gone there and asked the librarian for permission to look at the books, but I had an instinctive feeling that the library people would be in league with the school people. Instead, I foraged among my parents' books. The haul was thin. Only two of them interested me. There was a book called *Greek Myths and Legends*, a précis of Homer's

Iliad. I found it interesting not just for the stories themselves. For the first time I realised there was a land where the sun shone brightly, instead of perpetually through a veil of soot from the burning of soft coal. I also became aware that human deformity was not a necessary concomitant of life. A major difference from the way things are today and the way things were in the mid-1920s is the many instances one saw then of deformities associated with early industrial conditions.

The other book was of a very different kind. It was an introductory textbook on chemistry, about 250 pages long, which I read from cover to cover as best I could. Compared with the trivia of school classes, this book started a train of events which first secured my scholarship to Bingley Grammar School, which played a considerable role in taking me to Cambridge University, and which in the 1940s led me into fruitful research work on the origin of the chemical elements themselves.

The chemistry book was my father's. There were also in the house, tucked away in a remote cupboard, simple bits of chemical equipment which my father had purchased in earlier times. There were flasks and retorts, corks and a cork borer, glass tubing and a bunsen burner, together with a dozen or so bottles of reagents. From that moment on, until I became established at Bingley Grammar School, I undertook a sequence of steadily more complex experiments, advancing bit by bit through the chemistry text. Indeed, if I had continued my home experiments, granted adequate financial resources and space, I would either have become a tolerable experimenter or alternatively have blown myself to kingdom come.

Although I started modestly enough, experiments of a more violent type soon dominated my attention, with much employment of oxygen-rich substances like potassium chlorate. Making gunpowder was a natural, especially as older boys also made gunpowder. It was, in principle, easy to grind together charcoal, sulphur and potassium nitrate. I was canny enough to do the grinding in small quantities, which I discovered were not dangerous as long as the mixture could go off freely without being closely confined. The trick was to pack gunpowder inside the hollow barrel of some large key, and at this stage you really had to be mighty careful. Then you went outside and wanged the key as hard as you could from a distance into a stone wall. If a good mixing job had been done you got a satisfactory sharp explosion, which served to win for you a good deal of prestige among bystanders whom you had thoughtfully invited to watch the proceedings.

The experiments were carried out in the small kitchen of the house, which we called the scullery. My parents did not realise how hairy the experiments were becoming until one day I allowed a girl into the house on an occasion when my parents were out. I showed her one or two bits of alchemy, such as pouring sulphuric acid on sugar, a trick I used from time to time to light the bunsen burner when I ran out of matches. I then made the mistake of taking my eyes off the girl, only for a short time, I swear. She must have started mixing things at random with as sweeping a style as if she were baking. In next to no time there was a crack and a huge flare-up. Luckily neither of us was hurt physically, but the girl's dress was a wreck, and since the kitchen itself bore evidence of the flare-up there was no hiding what had happened. I suppose it was because at that time there was a fad for what the shops called 'chemistry sets', but which were really piffling stuff, that I was permitted – amazingly in retrospect – to persist, but only on the solemn condition that I admitted no one else to my seances.

The experiment I pursued with dogged persistence for over a year was illustrated towards the end of the chemistry text. For me it represented a compulsive dividing line between kid's stuff and adult stuff. It was the preparation of phosphine. The diagram in the book did it for me. There was a flask with two entry ports at the top, out of one of which a glass tube led under water. Emerging from the water were bubbles of phosphine, which turned into splendid smoke rings as they rose up in the air.

My first problem was that I didn't have adequate equipment, so I had to begin by saving up for several things. A day eventually came when I took the tram which ran along the valley to Bradford. I made my way from the tram terminal to Sunbridge Road, where the biggest chemist in Bradford was located – a wholesale chemist, I was informed, not that I could see anything wholesale in my intended purchases. Imagine yourself to be the assistant in that chemist's shop in Sunbridge Road in the late months of 1925. A boy of ten and a half comes in and fixes you with a gaze like the Ancient Mariner and says: 'Does 'ta 'ave a Woolf bottle?' Rather to my surprise, he did. It cost 3*s* 6*d*. 'Does 'ta 'ave any glass tubing?' was my next question. The assistant went away and came back with a veritable armful of glass tubing. My cup ranneth over with happiness, for to this point I'd been managing with only a few bits of glass tubing, bending the same bits into varying shapes in the flame of the bunsen burner according to the changing demands of each experiment. Here were riches beyond the dreams of avarice. 'Does 'ta 'ave any concentrated sulphuric acid?' was my next request. At this, the assistant at last looked me over with an element of misgiving, but I repeated compulsively: 'Does 'ta 'ave any concentrated sulphuric acid? H_2SO_4, tha knaws.'

The chemical formula must have done it, for the assistant now went away and eventually returned with a half-pint bottle of concentrated sulphuric acid. Can you imagine a small unknown boy walking into a chemist's shop today and thus securing a half-pint of concentrated H_2SO_4? To this point the chemist in Bingley, a kindly old fellow called Cranshaw, had always fobbed me off with dilute stuff offered in a small, green-ribbed poison bottle, saying with a gentle smile: 'I think this should do.' Yet even concentrated H_2SO_4 was simple stuff to handle compared to my projected preparation of phosphine. The delicious trouble with phosphine was that it would explode on contact with air, so that if you went ahead and prepared it without first flushing out your equipment with an inert gas, the whole shooting match was likely to go up in small pieces.

The book recommended persistent flushing out with ordinary town gas, but I didn't like the idea of filling my mother's small kitchen floor-to-ceiling with town gas and then cooking the phosphorus and potassium hydroxide with a bunsen burner. So after using just a little of the town gas, I relied on the form of explosion which became known in scientific circles in later times as the 'fizzle'. I decided the amount of oxygen left in the equipment would be small, so that if I made all the corks loose the explosive combination of phosphine and any remaining internal oxygen should dissipate itself in blowing out the corks. The day came at last when I was ready to go. Taking care that my parents were out, and that the corks were nicely loose, I slipped in the bunsen and let things cook, retreating to a safe distance myself. Things went as planned. There was a soft explosion which freed the corks, whereupon I rushed out of my hiding place and pressed them in more securely than before, arguing that the oxygen had gone now and therefore my equipment was satisfactorily flushed. Pretty soon the phosphine started to bubble up through the water, and there were my smoke rings, just as the book had said would happen.

I repeated the experiment two or three times more. My mother really did protest strenuously about it, because the phosphine stank out her kitchen terribly and took surely a week to clear itself. In later life I have always detested the smell and taste of garlic, and phosphine smells like garlic. A Swiss physicist once told me he and his wife had crossed the Atlantic in a boat carrying a cargo of garlic. Clearly he had never prepared phosphine in his youth.

But my landmark experiment with phosphine was still more than a year into the future when, coming up to the age of nine, I left Mornington Road School for the discovery of kingfishers' nests and for the study of the five-rise locks at Bingley. To this point I had three blank years to my credit in the war with the educational system. More and more I felt I was winning.

Chapter Five

I HAVE MENTIONED the nearby village of Eldwick on several occasions. Eldwick had a small school with about ninety pupils between the ages of five and fourteen. The school building had just two rooms – a small one for infants and a larger high room about thirty-five feet long which housed all the standards from I to VIII, with I, II, and III separated from IV to VIII by a curtain. When in full complement Eldwick village school had three teachers – a woman for the infants, a woman looking after standards I to III, and a male headteacher for standards IV to VIII. The school was often not in full complement, however, because one or other of the two women was almost perpetually off sick. The record of their exits and entrances was complex enough to put Shakespeare to shame.

The headteacher from around 1905 to the 1930s referred to himself as Tom Murgatroyd, although everybody else called him Tommy Murgatroyd. In my time he was in his late forties and he invariably wore plus fours. As it happened he had once been briefly on the same school staff as my mother, and so in the problem of coping with my determined exit from Mornington Road

School, he and Eldwick School were my mother's final backstop. To this point she had hesitated even to contemplate sending me to Eldwick, because it would be hard from Eldwick to climb onto the scholarship ladder. But now in the summer of 1924, without any other move left on the board, the position was essentially forced on her. So my mother approached Tommy Murgatroyd with whatever part of my rebellious life history she saw fit to tell him. Sometime before Eldwick school closed for the summer holiday at the end of July 1924 I was taken there. To my surprise Tommy Murgatroyd's establishment had a better look about it than I had seen before. As I quickly calculated the situation, this chap in the plus fours, with five standards on his hands, would have little time or motive to pester me. So, with the cautious agreement of all parties concerned, it was decided I would enter Eldwick School when it reopened in September.

My mother would soon have lost the limited measure of enthusiasm she'd managed to summon up had the report on Eldwick School, tendered at almost exactly this time by His Majesty's Inspector T.J.M. More, been available for her inspection. Dated 9 July 1924, it read:

> The teaching conditions indicated in the last report still exist. Until they are remedied it is impossible to expect that the children can be properly taught. The main room is awkward in several respects, and is indeed suitable only for a single class. At present an attempt is made by two teachers to teach eight standards in it.
>
> For the teachers, some of whom stay to dinner, there is no separate room, cloakroom or lavatory. The playground space is encroached upon by ladders, broken iron pipes, and coke and coal dumps. There seems to be no storeroom. The caretaker's cleaning gear is stored partly in the girls' cloakroom, which, even as a cloakroom, is inadequate.
>
> Many of the desks are too small for the children using

> them. In view of these discouraging conditions it is gratifying to be able to record an advance in certain directions ...

Plainly, winning a scholarship from Eldwick with its broken iron pipes and coal dumps was going to be no easy assignment, especially as the educational authorities of the West Riding of Yorkshire gave only about a dozen to the whole Bingley area. It was never apparent to me until recently why my parents made such a big thing out of my winning a scholarship to the grammar school. The reason, I discovered eventually, had an emotional component. At the age of eleven my father had won such a scholarship, but with his own father recently deceased he had been obliged to go to work to help support his mother and younger brother. There seems to have been an almost compulsive wish to compensate for things in my own generation.

Eldwick was the school I would brave the biting north wind in winter to reach; you turned sharp right at Brick Kiln Row to get there. The fact that I often accepted real physical hardship without complaint to reach Eldwick School shows that I wasn't really difficult. It was rather that even at an early age I couldn't stomach stupidity, however much the stupidity might be cloaked in adult authority.

If you could see Eldwick School today you would like it. It still stands in relation to the wild moorland just as it did in my time, but with the number of pupils expanded greatly to about 300. A few years back I opened the school's centennial jubilee. I took the opportunity of my visit to the district to tour around, looking at other schools over the whole Bingley region. Eldwick seemed to me the best of them all, although unfortunately it is confined nowadays to pupils up to the age of nine or ten. In my time there was just the main building as you turned in from the main road, through iron gates it is true, but lower and less prison-like than those at Mornington Road. If you turned right on entering you arrived immediately at the boys' playground, sloping from right to left, and if you turned left you arrived at the girls' playground, the two playgrounds being separated by the obligatory high wall, which was standard and regarded as essential by the educational authorities. The strange aspect of the morality of the time was that a teacher could burst your eardrums practically without comment, but if a girl had been made pregnant at school the uproar would have continued from the moment the pregnancy became visible to the delivery of the child, and the notoriety and disgrace of it would have vaulted out of the Aire Valley into half the county of Yorkshire.

At the end of the wall, as far from the school as possible, were the bogs, one on each side of the wall. Besides their more obvious utility value, the bogs had a significance I will now explain. As soon as the nights became frosty with the approach of winter, the older boys swilled a section of their playground with buckets of water so as to produce an icy surface by morning. Then they would launch themselves, preferably with a yell or roar, from the highest part of the playground at its roadside end in the direction of the bogs. Owing to the slope of the yard the sliding figure picked up speed as it went down the slippery black ice. Because of the curvature of the ground the figure would be turned gently to the left, and would thus avoid crashing into the bogs, but would collide instead with the high wall which separated the two playgrounds. I watched the sturdy sons of local farmers doing it scores of times – roar, pick up speed, crash.

Since I had missed essentially the whole of Standard III year at Mornington Road School I was started at Eldwick School again in Standard III, which meant that I began on the junior side of the curtain in the main schoolroom. But the headteacher's logbook records that on 5 January 1925 I was promoted to Standard IV on the senior side of the curtain, so rejoining my rightful age group. As the succeeding months unfolded I moved steadily up the desks by which the scholastic pecking order was defined. There was actually a good reason for the positioning of the sharper pupils in special desks, because the special desks were the ones most likely to catch the eye of a visiting inspector. I always enjoyed visiting inspectors. For one thing you could see your own teacher was edgy and that was good. For another thing your teacher, instead of wanting to keep you pegged down as on a normal day, seemed positively to welcome it if you were bouncy when the inspector asked questions. Gradually I came to see the reason why. The very worst thing, the most boring thing, for an inspector was to be faced by a sea of unresponsive children. If you even started a row, a row about anything at all, it made the inspector's day and he gave the school a good report. Gradually I came to see that this was a real trump card in my hand, as long as it was played with a bit of tact.

I was more popular with the girls at Eldwick School than I've ever been before or since, girls not only of my own age but right up to school-leaving age. Because of the open system it was easy when Tommy Murgatroyd was occupied elsewhere for girls to slip me their exercise books. I would quickly do their sums and then slip the exercise books back. In return, the girls would dry my clothes for me. We often arrived at school with sopping outer garments. In a smaller room adjacent to the main schoolroom was a big smoky boiler near which we were permitted to hang our clothes. The girls did much better at this – they were much better at pushing in than I was.

A disadvantage of the open classroom with all ages present is that an older boy can more easily come to have a down on a younger boy. Rather remarkably, during my two years at Eldwick School only one older boy tried to bully me. Over a period of about two months he set himself to waylay me in the afternoon on my way home and it became a tense battle of wits to avoid him. This period, in which I learned every wrinkle for varying my route between Eldwick and Gilstead, turned out to stand me in good stead three or four years later, by which time I had begun attendance at the grammar school. In the evening there would be homework to do, but since I could never see much point in labouring unduly on homework I was usually finished by 8.00 p.m., which left an hour before my mother would put on a bit of late supper, as she always did around 9.00. Often enough I would occupy the intervening hour by taking a walk, and since the return journey to Eldwick took just on the hour, I would walk there by one route and return by another.

One evening after dark I was coming into Eldwick by an unmade road and had arrived at the first gas lamps. As I came under the light, I heard an ominous voice say, '*That's* 'im.' Perhaps forty yards away to my right down a lane I saw two hulking figures, both evidently lads much older than I was. My former experience with the bully told me this was no moment for elegant delay. Instantly I took to my heels, so quickly indeed that I must have opened up another thirty to forty yards before the two figures reacted. The lights of Eldwick lay ahead. If I could reach a certain point where there were several shops, the bus stop and the local policeman's house, I felt I would be safe. Because I really knew the ground, and because of my lead, I made it. Then I stopped in the bright light of one of the shops and waited for the two figures to reach me. They were youths of about seventeen whom I hadn't seen before. 'Does ta know —?' one of them asked with extreme truculence. (I have unfortunately forgotten the girl's name.) 'Naw, ah doan't knaw —,' I replied, speaking as much in the dialect as possible. 'Well, if tha does, we'll beat the hell out of tha,' offered the second youth unhelpfully. Then the absurdity of a fourteen-year-old boy depriving them of a girl who was good enough for both must have struck home, and as if a switch had been pressed they became friendly, telling me they'd been robbed of the girl, but they didn't know by whom: 'If tha 'ears tell, just let us knaw,' was the last shot.

The injuries this age group inflicted on each other in their pursuit of girls were something to behold. One evening after dark several years earlier, the call had gone out among us much younger village boys that a real 'feight' was on. A guide escorted us at a determined run to the spot, to my surprise taking the turning down Primrose Lane past my own house to where the big gates into the Milnerfield Estate were located. The road was unmade at that time, and two hefty-looking figures were sprawled there in the dirt under a gas lamp, seeking to choke the lives out of each other. The youth who appeared to be getting the worst of it had his face streaked with blood and one of his eyes was black and had swollen to the size of a golfball.

'It's Stalker,' breathed a ghoul next to me in hushed fascination. Stalker was a handsome fellow, and it was easy to guess he'd 'robbed' his incensed opponent. How the triangular affair eventually turned out I never learned, essentially because to us the affair itself seemed unimportant. It was the 'feight' which really mattered. The spot where the two figures had sprawled in the dirt lay in the very middle of the ancient traders' route between the Aire and Wharfe Valleys, the route dating back to Domesday.

Tommy Murgatroyd lived for his garden. With considerable ingenuity he had persuaded the local Education Committee to allow him to use the garden for instructional purposes, I suppose because it was thought sensible that the sons and daughters of farmers, who were themselves likely to become farmers, should be taught how to grow vegetables. On every occasion when the weather was remotely tolerable, he had most of the boys out in the garden, set to some job or other. Since the older boys were robust, as their crashing into the playground wall demonstrated, the school made a fine and handy labour force. Tommy Murgatroyd's garden was always in the pink of condition.

In my judgement some people are born with skeletons suited to gardening and others are not. I was one who was not. So here I played my school-inspector card. In lieu of gardening, I did assigned school tasks – sums and so on. Because Tommy Murgatroyd could make the tasks sound almost like punishments he lost no face with the other children over the arrangement and it suited both of us, especially as I was well-nigh useless as a gardener.

Possibly it was usual for there to be lessons in gardening at village schools generally, but my experience at other schools had not led me to expect it. The thing struck even my child's mind as curious, to the extent that clear memories of it have persisted for sixty years. It was beyond my perception, however, to realise just how far gone and acute the situation really was, as Tommy Murgatroyd's logbook makes clear – to the point of painful hilarity. It was already in full cry ten years before my time:

> An extra gardening lesson was taken today to make up for the one lost on 21 November, through fog.
>
> Miss Carrodus had to leave school today through illness.
>
> Miss Dawson left school today with very severe toothache.
>
> Gardening could not be taken today owing to the absence of Miss Dawson.
>
> An extra gardening lesson was taken today to make up for the one omitted Feb 8.
>
> An extra gardening lesson was taken today to make up for the one omitted March 2.
>
> Miss Dawson was absent, visiting dentist.

> Gardening is impossible this p.m. owing to snow and sleet.

Since the gardening fetish must have been known to my mother, it becomes clear why she was sceptical of Eldwick School serving as a red-hot establishment for the winning of scholarships. Precisely the same two issues, the illness of the women teachers and his garden, were still Tommy Murgatroyd's main concern in my own time, as the following contemporary extracts from his logbook demonstrate:

> Gardening is impossible owing to fog and frost.
> Miss Smales absent today, ill.
> " " is absent with influenza.
> An extra gardening lesson was taken this morning to make up for the one lost Tuesday.
> Miss Hey left sick at 10 a.m.
> Gardening could not be taken today owing to the absence of Miss Hey.
> Gardening is impossible today. It is V. Wet.
> Owing to a rainstorm only 53 children were present out of 90.
> Gardening outside is impossible.
> Miss Smales has been absent today with bad cold.
> Gardening again impossible owing to rain.

The time eventually came on a cold Saturday morning in mid-February 1926 for me to take the West Riding County Minor Scholarship Examination. The examination was the same for every child in the West Riding of Yorkshire. If you won a scholarship you were sent to the nearest grammar school. This was an advantage over winning one of the half-a-dozen scholarships the Governors of Bingley Grammar School gave each year on their own account, because if your parents moved from one district to another you simply transferred from one grammar school to another. If my parents had moved into Bradford, for example, I might well have been transferred to Bradford Grammar, assuming I won one of the dozen or so scholarships awarded each year to the Bingley district with its population, including outlying villages, of about 20,000. I was of minimum age, ten, whereas you were permitted to take the examination up to twelve. So if I failed, I was assured that there would be two more chances.

The pupils at schools in the town itself, like Mornington Road, took the examination in their own classrooms, which gave them a considerable advantage over us children from the rural areas, who were herded together into whatever space could be made available. I was told to go to a school close by Holy Trinity Church, then a high-spired black-grimed building at the hub of the collection of streets of back-to-back houses which constituted the poorer, eastern part of Bingley. I remember it seemed exceptionally cold as I made my way, I think alone, down from Gilstead into the outskirts of Bingley. I crossed the canal bridge and turned right into a street with the unpromising name of Dub Lane. A hundred yards along Dub Lane I turned sharp left, and then up a flight of steps into the streets with the back-to-back houses, arriving a few moments later at Holy Trinity Church, and at a room with a high ceiling which had been cleared to accommodate what seemed to me a multitude of desks where an apparently monstrous horde of children was assembled. The scene was about as different as was possible from the small Eldwick School.

The examination room was cold that winter day. Perhaps being a Saturday morning the school boiler was not working properly. You could say a fair amount of heat was put out by the children themselves and this had to be true, say sixty watts a child, but the high roof of the room, allowing the warmer air to rise way above us, largely cancelled this self-sustaining effect. I know I felt terribly leaden-footed in everything I was called on to do: slow to find my place in the throng, slow to answer the questions that were asked. In recent years a German chess grandmaster walked out in despair from a candidates' match for the World Championship because he was called on to play in poor surroundings, with district trains rattling past most of the time. His opponent was a Soviet grandmaster who conveniently happened to be deaf, so it was widely believed that the venue had been arranged by the KGB. My situation was not dissimilar, although I could make no such spectacular claim as to its cause.

The arithmetic paper had two parts. Part 1 said 'Answer only 4 questions,' and Part 2 said 'Answer No. 6 and 3 others.' The time allowed was one hour and twenty minutes. For a trained child it would not have caused much trouble, but for a child sporting my formidable truancy record from a country school whose headteacher had a gardening fetish that was quite out of control, the paper was something of a corker. The easy opener read:

> 1) (a) $\frac{5}{12} + \frac{7}{15}$, (b) ($\frac{3}{5}$ of $3\frac{1}{5}$) − $1\frac{11}{15}$ Divide (a) by (b).

The last shot was:

> 10) A boy was told to multiply the sum of 0.028 and a second number by 0.035. Instead of this he multiplied the second number only by 0.035 and then added 0.028 to the product. His result was 0.05012. What result should he have obtained if he had done as he was told?

Nobody had ever told me the trick for answering questions like this last one. It is simple: name the quantity you require, which is to say give the unknown number a name, x say, and work it out from there. It was only some months after the examination that I discovered this trick, and then I felt really angry at having been tricked myself.

Following the arithmetic paper we were required to answer questions in English grammar and to write an essay. Throughout my schooldays I was always unenthusiastic about English grammar. It was what I called a daft subject. So I did it because I was required to do it and for no other reason. My point of view was that either you knew how to write and talk or you didn't, a view confirmed in later years by a friend in the English Faculty at Cambridge who said: 'Every child of eight has an almost perfect command of syntax in speech but not of word order or vocabulary.' It would be interesting to know how it first came about that grammar became such a feature of so-called elementary education. The thing must have started on somebody's arbitrary say-so, and having become established it simply went on and on. One might rather say the distinguishing feature of the English language is the lack of grammar, with word order and the subtle use of vocabulary taking its place. One can also say that pedagogues do not invent language. New uses in language spring from the instinctive perceptions of people needing to express an idea or an emotion which cannot be expressed adequately by previous usages, as in the famous example when Chris Marlowe broke suddenly through to the discovery of blank verse in his play *The Tragicall History of Dr Faustus*.

The subjects offered as topics for an essay were distinctly peculiar. As I think I remarked before, the examination took place in early 1926, shortly after the signing of the Locarno Pact. There was no offer of this grandiose subject as a topic for an essay. Instead there was the following absurdity, to which nobody I ever talked with afterwards was able to offer much of an answer: 'Write a short story which brings in the following: As Freddy stepped out of the train, his sister ran to greet him. "How you have grown," she said, and then, "What! Have you left your bag behind on this day of all days?"' Months, even years after the examination I puzzled away to myself over what Freddy had been up to. But I never managed to fit the growing and the bag and the day of all days together into a plausible scenario.

During the arithmetic paper I was conscious of being unaccountably slow. I did only five questions out of the required eight, which was disappointing since in arithmetic I usually worked rather quickly. During the English paper I was vaguely conscious of writing a lot of nonsense, which I tried to pass off to myself with the assurance that the paper itself really was a lot of nonsence. The very next morning I woke with my face feeling a mile wide. When my mother brought a mirror I laughed unrestrainably, even though laughing was quite painful. I was down with an attack of mumps, an attack which had been an unsuspected joker in the pack throughout the morning in the chilling environment of the examination hall.

Because I had done only five arithmetic questions, and because I suspected my English paper was harum-scarum, I insisted to my parents that I'd done badly. But my father was not so sure. I'd brought the arithmetic paper home with all my answers jotted in the margin. It proved they were uniformly correct, so that although I'd done only a fraction of what I'd been asked to do everything was properly done, which an examiner might be expected to judge a hopeful sign from a child who was as young as it was possible to be for the scholarship examination. It never occurred to my parents to obtain a doctor's certificate and to ask Tommy Murgatroyd to forward it to the educational authority. I doubt it would have done much good if they had. Viruses were still unknown as the cause of many childhood illnesses, which were then seen as mysteries one simply came to accept. The general idea was that you were 'well' up to the outbreak of clinical symptoms. So the idea would be that I was 'well' – lucky for me, people would have said –

during the examination itself and had only become 'ill' the following day.

Results appeared some two months later. If you won a scholarship the school received a coloured letter, blue I think. Otherwise the letter was white. There was no blue letter at Eldwick School. I realised it the moment Tommy Murgatroyd came in one morning with the relevant letters. So I'd failed and that was that. The situation had to be accepted both at home and at school. Yet my father had plenty to talk about in connection with the examination, because as soon as the results became known a considerable scandal broke loose. Results everywhere in the mid-Aire Valley were poor, with no more than half the usual number of scholarships awarded to the Bingley area – six instead of the usual ten or more. Other districts in the West Riding had extremely large numbers, however, which raised the possibility, nay the certainty, that there had been serious cheating. The scandal escalated rapidly, with members of the Bingley town council threatening action against the county. In these circumstances it became inevitable that the county education authority took a second look at children from the Bingley area. I know from later personal experience that there is all the difference in the world between the routine marking of examination papers and the hunting through of examination papers on the look-out for exceptional cases. The papers of a young candidate who wrote quite deliriously on the English paper but was almost totally precise in the arithmetic paper must surely have caught the eye. About three weeks after the first announcement there came a request through Tommy Murgatroyd that I should present myself to the grammar school for an interview with the headmaster there.

The headmaster, Alan Smailes, had come through the Mathematical Tripos at Cambridge. Yet I do not recall him asking anything at all about arithmetic. He asked me to read a passage from a book, which I did easily enough.

Then he asked what books I had read myself. In retrospect it is clear that Smailes had been requested by the county authority to verify that I really was in possession of my faculties. I still never thought to tell him of the mumps, but I did tell him about the chemistry book I'd read, and about books on stars I'd borrowed from the public library. Pretty soon he packed me off for a word with the chemistry master. Herbert Haigh was in his thirties, a dark-haired man with a pleasant face who had received terrible wounds in the 1914–18 war. In later years he told me an incompetent nurse had poured caustic on the wounds, thinking it a disinfectant. At the height of the depression he bought chemistry books out of his own pocket to help those of us who were then seeking entry to universities. He was the only teacher I ever came across who kept perfect discipline in class without any physical demonstration or even a harsh word. On this occasion he asked me what experiments I'd been doing, and it was natural for me to tell him about the phosphine preparation I described in the previous chapter. He was incredulous and demanded to know how I'd done it. So I launched into a description of the loose corks and the fizzle of an explosion I'd provoked. At this a smile flashed across his face and with twinkling eyes he said: 'Well, you'll not be doing that here.'

I pondered this remark on my way home, and thought it might mean I'd won the scholarship after all. In a curiously roundabout way I had. A blue-coloured letter appeared at Eldwick School shortly afterwards and my name eventually went up in gilt letters on a board in the schoolroom that held all the scholarship winners there had been in the history of the school – at that time about twenty.

Chapter Six

I BEGAN ATTENDANCE at Bingley Grammar School in September 1926, almost four centuries after the school was founded in 1529. The school must have been active in around 1645, when Cromwell had his considerable nest of supporters in Bingley. No such profound historic thoughts entered my head, however. The most immediate effect for me was that I now had to walk nearly eight miles each day instead of five. I continued to return home for lunch since there were no organised school meals. The annual rainfall for the district being about thirty-five inches I must have got wet – sometimes soaked, sometimes merely damp – on hundreds of occasions over the seven years from eleven to eighteen, by which time I had walked a total of some 10,000 miles. The odd thing is I have no memory of sitting damp and miserable at school, although I do remember exceptionally rainy periods when I set out from home wishing it would be fine on at least one day in the week.

My father maintained a never-ending struggle with the West Riding educational authorities. In contrast to their generosity in every other respect, the authorities were very rigid about bus fares. The rule was that a scholarship holder who lived more than two miles from school could claim transport costs. The distance from our house to the grammar school along the shortest route by which you could take a vehicle was within a cat's whisker of two miles. It is actually so close that it would need a commission of enquiry to decide the matter, and the outcome might even turn on which classroom and building at the school you were heading for. The shortest route for vehicles from Gilstead went downwards at a gentle angle past the Cottage Hospital. It turned a corner, and there on the left was a largish house with a walled garden where a girl lived who at about that time married Wally Hammond, the great English batsman. The streets of Bingley were lined for the occasion by thousands of people, because a wild and absurd rumour was abroad that Wally Hammond was going to ditch his career with Gloucestershire and come to play cricket for the town of Bingley. Then you went gently upwards and around a long bend to Park Road, where a horse trough stood on an open bit of ground – my relative Fred Jackson used to pad around its iron rim in triumph until one day he slipped and broke a front tooth clean across – then left down Park Road into Bingley until you came to the T-junction at the Bradford-to-Keighley road just by Leach's the sports goods shop, which used to stock Meccano sets and Hornby trains but is now given over to the sale of baby wool – and there you turned right and continued for two-thirds of a mile until you reached the grammar school.

This was my father's route. But the educational authorities probably argued that there was a shorter walking route. Actually, there was – branching sharply left at the Cottage Hospital and down past the Catholic school, whose pupils were stoned periodically. This brought you to a cliff-like drop of fifty feet, which at that time you had to scramble down. Then you continued along and around streets with high-sounding names like

Belgrave Road, but which were actually back-to-back houses, until you reached Mornington Road School. Here you circumnavigated the high wall enclosing first the girls' and then the boys' playground until you reached the iron gates, where you stopped for a moment to deliver a big ha-ha. Reaching Mornington Road proper you then turned right and continued across Park Road, passing the mill where nowadays Damart clothing is manufactured. Down a short, unmade track you came to the Leeds-to-Liverpool canal, precisely at the once famous five-rise locks I had studied so carefully in earlier years. After crossing the canal, pausing to gaze in awe deep down into the locks, you turned right and followed a narrow lane that took you under the railway through a long ginel smelling not unlike a urinal. Eventually the ginel debouched onto the Bingley-to-Keighley road, more or less opposite the parish church. Turning right you finally reached the grammar school in about a third of a mile.

This, apparently, was the route the educational authorities wanted me to take. It had the advantage that once a week or so my walk home in the afternoon chanced to coincide with the passage of a high-speed boat train. Many were the occasions in winter when I saw brightly lit carriages sweep past and wondered if the day would come when I would take the train myself to join a boat at Southampton bound for the United States. This cherished dream never became reality, since by the time I eventually visited the United States aeroplanes had largely replaced boats for transatlantic travel. Nobody as far as I recall ever predicted the use of aeroplanes for mass transportation, at any rate over large distances – all the talk in my youth was of airships. This notable failure to foresee the march of technology has made me sceptical of technological prediction, which is fraught with uncertainty in every field because of unexpected discoveries and unexpected snags. It is not so hard to foretell that such-and-such will be possible in the future, but the best technical way to achieve it is very difficult to judge in advance of events.

The school uniform was not obligatory, and in those times of depression nobody wore it. But we were required to wear the school cap. For a year or two I did so with reluctance, until going bare-headed became common generally. The cap often got me into 'feights' I would have preferred to avoid, a point in the bus-fare controversy the education authorities had presumably failed to consider. If they wanted to toughen up their scholarship boys this was certainly the way to do it, for a grammar school cap was like a red rag to a bull to the boys from every intervening school on my route. I was never actually stoned like the Catholic children, but the 'feights' would have been a daily occurrence if I hadn't displayed a little of the subtlety in varying my route that I'd developed in earlier years.

Actually, I agreed with the brusque lads from the intervening schools. The cap was a mark of class distinction which I disliked as much as they did. I was still two or three years away from reading the works of George Bernard Shaw, but I was already struggling towards a concept which Shaw expresses admirably towards the end of his play *Arms and the Man*. The Swiss mercenary Captain Bluntschli is in competition with Sergius the Balkan aristocrat as to which of them has the greatest possessions and the highest social standing. Bluntschli draws himself up and says: 'My rank is the highest known.' When this immediately rivets the attention of everybody on stage, Bluntschi continues: 'I am a free citizen of Switzerland.' Throughout my life I have never ceased to regret that such a point of view is not ingrained deeply within the British people. Had it been, I doubt whether the position of Britain in the world would ever have retreated from the high point it once occupied.

When I began attendance at Bingley Grammar I tried

to persuade myself that changing schools would have no effect on my relationships with the village boys. Yet it did. Not through money or through a cap or an old school tie, but through ideas developing in the head, a process which had begun already by the time I was coming up to ten. A story from those earlier years may be worth telling since it had some effect on my life, perhaps subconsciously a dominating effect.

Once we returned to school in the autumn – at the time in question it must have been Eldwick School for me – there were set activities we engaged in from year to year as standard procedures. One was to begin collecting wood for the village bonfire on Guy Fawkes' night. Another was a game we played every fine night over a period of three or four weeks, pretty well through the month of October, once the evenings became dark enough. A band of us, perhaps twenty strong, divided into two halves. We had a centre point by a particular gas lamp with a fine, large piece of sandstone below it, which is there still today. One half of us went off into the darkness and was given a few minutes' start. Then the other half went after them, but leaving behind a guard stationed perhaps fifty yards from the sandstone block. If any member of the search party came near enough to recognise you and call out your name correctly, that counted one up to the search party, but if you managed to get back to the sandstone block without being recognised, that was one up to the field party. We made the game self-adjusting, in the sense that we learnt to judge the distance of the guards from the sandstone block so as to ensure that the tallies came out fairly evenly. The roles of the two parties were alternated from night to night. We called the game by the unlikely name of 'Bed Socks', obviously a corruption of something or other. I just grew up with the name and accepted it, without ever thinking it a problem as I would have done if something physical had been involved. Already at the age of nine I felt that the world of people and their ways was too complex and arbitrary to be sorted out, unlike the world of things, which seemed to have an attainable rationality to it.

I happened to be in the field party one perfect star-lit night. I had a special friend I went about with most of the time. Even to this day I'm pretty sure of the route we took from the sandstone block. We ran off about twenty yards down Primrose Lane and then ducked left into the darkness of the 'Sparable', along which we continued to its second sharp-angled turn. Then we climbed a wall, low on our side but with a biggish drop for us on the opposite side, then down into the valley where the stream ran which passed through the Milnerfield Estate and on the banks of which I'd found the ill-fated kingfisher's nest. There was first a wood and then a wall over into the 'bull field' of Robinson's farm. Up the bull field and over into the roadway close to where Herbert Haigh, the chemistry master at Bingley Grammar School, would come to live a year or two later. Then we doubled back to the sandstone block in the shelter of more of the fields of Robinson's farm.

When on top of a wall that perfect star-lit night I seemed to be in contact with the sky instead of the earth, a sky powdered from horizon to horizon with thousands of points of light, which on that particular dry, frosty night were unusually bright. We were out for perhaps an hour and a half, and as time went on I became more and more aware – awed, I suppose – of the heavens. By the time I arrived back at the sandstone block I had made a resolve. I remember standing on the block and looking upwards and deciding that I would find out what those things up there were.

This resolve became more apposite when I reached the age of thirty than it was immediately. Even so, we had an old encyclopaedia in the home with simple articles on stars and planets. And in 1927 the book *Stars and Atoms* by Eddington became available in the town library, which to me was another big turning point. At the age of ten or eleven I tried to tell my friends in the village something of all this, but either they weren't interested or they were so incredulous as to be derisive, which indicated that a barrier was inevitably opening up between us, quite apart from any difference in the schools we attended.

The way people enter our lives with apparently the tightest of relationships, which are then gradually but inexorably dissolved away by age, by a divergence of interests, or by external events over which we have no control, is for me one of the saddest aspects of things. You have no wish for it to be so but you are powerless to stop it from happening. Even the relationship with parents, which seems so overwhelmingly strong in our earliest years, is first weakened bit by bit as we 'go out into the world', as one says, and is finally terminated by death. Likewise, the seemingly unbreakable relationships with our own children are steadily weakened as they themselves go out into the world. Parents may see their grown children every few days if they all chance to live in the same district, or every few months if in the same country, and the feeling is always that nothing has changed. But it has, just as it had for my relationship with my friends in the village.

Like bits of jetsam in a fast-flowing river we come together and are then parted by the flow of events. There is just one relationship which can, and which does in many instances, stand rock solid against this swirling kaleidoscope, the bond between husband and wife. It is a curious thought – if we happen to be among the lucky ones for whom this relationship becomes a reality – that we go through our youth with relationships to parents, friends, teachers all seemingly of dominant importance, and yet the person who is to mean most in our lives has not yet appeared, as it would be in a play if the most important character did not come on stage until the second act.

All school classes I had attended to this point had been mixed. At the grammar school, however, the sexes were rigorously separated in class as well as on the playground. Although the girls' school was immediately adjacent to the boys', over seven years I did not have a single conversation with any girl, as I had done so often when doing sums for girls at Eldwick. Somewhere around 1930 a new building for the girls was put up and was even joined physically to the boys' school. But throughout my time there were always locked doors shrouded by a big, black, impenetrable curtain across the joining corridor. In later years when I described this situation in a speech day address to a later generation of pupils at Bingley Grammar, then happily mixed, there was merriment from the boys and girls sitting interspersed in the audience. What really brought the house down on that later occasion was the case of my relative Biddy Jackson, who was severely reprimanded by her headmistress for walking to school on the public highway beside Bill Jackson, her cousin.

Early in the first term at the grammar school the members of my class were given a kind of pecking order test, and I was sixteenth out of thirty-two. The stronger scholarship holders were ahead of me, as were a few scholarship holders who had come into the Bingley area from outside, and some of the fee-paying pupils who had already been at the school for a year or more. Most of the fee-payers were from better-off homes than the scholarship boys. Indeed the historic *raison d'être* for the school was to provide education for those who could afford it, with scholarship holders introduced in ones and twos at first, and in my time in about a half-and-half distribution. As one might have expected, the fee-payers were less uniform in ability than the scholarship boys, with the best being very good and the worst not so good. My position in the middle of the class, called 'forms' now instead of 'standards', was thus about right. The annual intake of schoolchildren for the whole Bingley area must have been in the region of 400. So I was sixteenth in about 400, which was a fair reflection on the irregularity of my education to this point. Or in terms of population, I was sixteenth in the annual output of children in a town of about 20,000.

Let me interpolate what a thorough investigation of standards would have revealed. There were at that time about 500 Fellows of the Royal Society of London, elected over the years on grounds of scientific merit from the Commonwealth as well as from the United Kingom. The election rate was about twenty-five new Fellows each year out of an educated group of about 100 million people, for a production rate for the whole Commonwealth of about one Fellow per four million people per year. The production rate for scientists of international repute was of a still lower order of magnitude, say one per 100 million people per year. It will therefore be clear how important it was to have no idea at all of the length of the road ahead if ever I were to become a scientist, which by now was beginning to suggest itself to my mind. The way to perceive the road ahead is not in terms of a far distant goal, but as a sequence of nearer steps by which you aim to improve yourself by a single order of magnitude at each stage. This is just the way mountaineers scale a high peak. The trick is to divide the route into a sequence of smaller objectives, otherwise the whole would seem overpoweringly vast.

By the end of the first term I had improved my form position to fifth, by the end of the second term to second, and by the end of the year to first, thus pulling up one of the many orders of magnitude I had to go. In the following year my positions were first, first and second, but in the third year they became first, second and third, which led to some disagreement with my parents who probably felt I wasn't trying hard enough, which in some degree was true.

There were several reasons why I appeared to be in decline. A simple reason was that I always had to overcome a fairish handicap in not being able to draw. In the term when I was third, my percentage in drawing was forty-seven, while the top marks were in the seventies. This cost me two or three points when the average percentage for all subjects was taken. But more importantly, I had ceased by the time I was thirteen to bother much with homework, which carried half the weight in our results. I preferred to score seven or eight out of ten for homework done quickly rather than spend a further hour or more in scoring an extra mark. There was a boy who came in from outside the Bingley area during this third year who simply slaved at his homework, and good luck to you, I thought, because it won't do you the slightest good when the real examinations of the matriculation year begin (the equivalent of modern O levels).

By the age of thirteen I had begun to read widely – borrowing the books from the town library – not only science books like Eddington's *Stars and Atoms*, but even such far-ranging and unlikely works as T.E. Lawrence's *Seven Pillars of Wisdom.* I made a considerable effort to trace Lawrence's activities in detail, finding some of his episodes cloudy. When claims were made many years later that certain of the episodes might not have happened, I wasn't altogether surprised. My parents felt this extra-curricular reading to be unwise, since they would have liked me to remain a bright and shining first, an example to all beholders. I remained deaf to their protestations, however, preferring obstinately to trust my own judgement.

Another possible reason for my easing off was that I didn't particularly like the form-master in the third year. While he had good qualities, there was an irrational irritability in him which showed itself by a perpetual nagging of particular boys. A day came when a big lad higher up the school than I was, provoked beyond bearing, felled him good and proper. Although this was represented to us as a crime Agatha Christie might be expected to write about, I felt it was long overdue.

Looking back over my time in the educational system I would say that the attitude of pupils towards teachers who became angry and violent was almost always fair-minded and psychologically accurate. Charlie Hulme, our English teacher, was a big, intrinsically gentle chap whom we teased unmercifully. Whenever we did readings of a Shakespeare play with the parts allotted to the class there were invariably cries of, 'Please sir, I want to be a lewd strumpet.' The cries were repeated *ad nauseam* until Hulme let out a roar, followed by a frenzied tour up and down the aisles between the desks aiming blows randomly as he went. Then there was a smallish boy, Tich Taylor, who carried a red diary in the breast pocket of his coat. Whenever Hulme told us some book or other was important, Taylor would slip out his diary and say: 'Please, sir, I have a little book ...' which was usually good enough to start an enraged tour, beginning in Taylor's direction but spreading like a tornado through the classroom. Nobody felt the slightest ill-will for any random blow they might receive in these periodic uproars, and Hulme was one of the best-liked teachers in the school.

The anger of Eddie Dodd, a fiery little Welshman, the senior master after Smailes, was something to behold. Dodd was our history and Latin teacher. One, or possibly two of his younger brothers became university professors, and my suspicion is that our Dodd might well have done the same had there not been economic reasons why the eldest brother in the family had to secure a job as soon as possible. He was the most erudite person I came across in my schooldays, and as befitted his intellectual qualities his anger had nothing down-to-earth about it.

Anger was not, in his view, something to be dispersed lightly. It was reserved for ludicrous mistakes, such as claiming Caesar to be a Gaul, or the Diet of Worms a new medical treatment. This sort of anger from a teacher never troubled me unduly, even though on occasions I found myself at the receiving end of it, especially as Dodd was my form-master through my last three years at school. Almost all my early perceptions outside science I owed to him.

I didn't worry too much about boys who sought the top position in the class through meticulously prepared homework, but there was one boy in the class whom I did watch closely, and if he had begun to beat me consistently all such extra-curricular activities as the *Seven Pillars of Wisdom* would instantly have gone out of the window. His name was Chester. I can't remember his christian name, largely, I think, because it was never used. He was dark-haired with a rather round head, as I recall, and more robust than I was. He was always quiet and friendly, but neither I nor anybody else I can remember ever penetrated a sort of withdrawn reserve. Mostly one knew the home background of the boys, certainly of any who were outstanding either in sport or in their work. Yet I never learned anything of Chester's background. It was consistent with his having been given a brief opportunity by a mother who was a war widow, such as might have been my own case if my father had not survived the Ludendorff attack of 21 March 1918. Be this as it may, Chester left school, despite great promise, immediately after the matriculation examination. He took a job in an industrial chemical company. Years later I learned he had risen to become its manager, which was no surprise at all. He treated the educational system more ruthlessly than ever I did, by paring down the subjects he would need for the matriculation examination to their bare bones, and these subjects he went after with unremitting determination. For instance, only one foreign language was required, which at our school meant either French or Latin. Quite why Chester chose Latin I never learned, but having chosen it I could never touch him. In my second year my class positions in Latin were first in each term, but in my third year Chester toppled me and I couldn't cope with the challenge, coming second in each term.

Chemistry was another of Chester's special choices, but here I considered any degree of effort to stay top was not only desirable but essential. Over the same six terms the honours were equal between us. It was a dogfight down almost to the last mark, with neither of us giving or receiving any quarter.

Physics during my first three years was a non-inspirational subject, and so it must have been for Chester, otherwise I would surely have made more effort at it. The experiments we were asked to do required neither planning nor dexterity. You did the experiment and then you wrote it up. Worse, you drew diagrams to show what you had done, and my drawings were pretty poor as usual. My class positions in physics over the same six terms were between third and sixth. Actually, there was not much to separate the sheep from the goats, since I had eighty percent even in sixth place. Since the work was straightforward, the marks were all crammed together between eighty and ninety percent, with those who took most pains over drawing and homework securing the highest places.

At the end of the third year, three or four of us skipped the normal fourth year, so arriving in the form destined for the matriculation examination a year earlier than usual. I thus began my fourth year at the grammar school eighteen months younger than the average age for the class, instead of six months younger as had formerly been the situation. No more reading of library books, for now I had the opportunity to see if I could lift myself by another order of magnitude. My class positions in my fourth year for the two terms before the matriculation examination were:

All subjects	4,2
Chemistry	5,1
Physics	1,1

Although the standards were as yet nothing to speak of, these placings were beginning to become significant, really more significant than the public examinations themselves. They demonstrated an ability to increase pace, with the results in physics perhaps of most interest. The hope was that, if I could spurt once, I could spurt twice or perhaps three times as levels of difficulty continued to rise.

I was just on my fifteenth birthday when the time eventually came for the matriculation examination. We were not specially drilled in the kind of questions to expect. Indeed, I do not recall our being shown the papers which had been set in previous years. So it was all rather like shooting at an unseen target, when high scores are not to be expected. This relaxed policy was, I suppose, consistent with the history of the school as an establishment for the education of the children of the well-to-do, who must not be put through the hoop too severely. It was not a policy likely to secure optimum results; the outcome for a class of thirty-odd would typically be about five matriculations, fifteen awards of what was known as the School Leaving Certificate, and for the rest, nothing. Such an easy-going attitude would surely be impossible today, but in times when matriculation was sought by pupils as a complete entrance qualification to universities, five out of thirty would be about right.

A paper-backed book of the results of the examination could be ordered through the school, with delivery at your home promised for the official announcement date in late August. I didn't order a book. Nor at any time to the end of the public examinations I sat in my youth did I ever make special arrangements for results to be sent to me. It was a sort of superstition, like touching wood, or like not counting your chickens before they were hatched, or like the old saying that no news is good news. There was another boy in the village who was involved, a boy whom I'd caught up when I jumped the fourth year. I was passing his house when the mother, a small ginger-haired woman, shouted: 'You've matricked. But Stanley has only certificated.' She invited me inside the house and I tried not to appear over-pleased. I looked through the results book and saw that Chester had also 'matricked'. Unfortunately I was never to see him again.

Just over fifteen years old, I returned to Bingley Grammar in September 1930, to find myself now in a different regime. Over the past four years I'd been taught systematically, subject by subject, according to a specified time-table. But this discipline could continue no longer, because the school had no special teachers for its sixth form. There were only eight regular teachers to about 200 pupils, so instruction in the sixth form had necessarily to be sporadic, extremely so in mathematics because in addition to teaching the younger pupils Alan Smailes had his administrative duties as headmaster to attend to as a first priority. In effect, the sixth form was an addition tacked onto a school where pupils traditionally left immediately after the matriculation examination. Laboratory space was also a problem, with the main laboratories occupied by junior classes for most of the time.

This was hardly a favourable situation for winning a university scholarship. But as a training ground for research it was surely excellent to be thrown heavily on our own resources in this way. The system was for us to be given tasks by the masters, which we set about solving in the spirit of research projects. Formal lessons were comparatively few and our number was so small that a lesson in chemistry, for example, would be attended by everybody aiming at the Higher Certificate (A level), irrespective of which particular year you were in. The other two pupils following a similar path to myself happened to be my relative Fred Jackson, the one who broke a tooth padding around the horse trough in Park Road, and a big strong lad with whom I would eventually do quite a bit of hill-walking, Edward Foster. Fred Jackson was in the same year as myself, but Edward Foster was a year ahead, and it was he who now set the pace for us.

Situated off both the main chemistry and physics laboratories were smaller rooms, reminiscent of my mother's kitchen but somewhat larger. We were given these rooms in which to set up our own laboratories; this procedure had the advantage that the time we could spend in our little private laboratories was almost unlimited. Money for equipment and chemicals was always a problem, just as it had been when I bought my Woolf bottle for 3*s* 6*d*. It was impossible for the school to buy all the chemicals we might need, so in organic chemistry especially we often had to synthesize even the reagents before we could begin assigned experiments – not the quickest way to prepare for the Higher Certificate, but mighty good for our eventual self-reliance. Edward Foster was to become a Reader in Physics at Imperial College, London, while Fred Jackson became the Head of a strong cardiac department at Newcastle General Hospital.

Major Scholarships, as they were called, were awarded by the West Riding educational authorities on the results of the Higher Certificate examination, and there were also national State Scholarships. Few counties were as generous as Yorkshire in education matters, so the competition nationwide for State Scholarships was very keen, forcing a higher standard than in the county. I was told that a sixty-seven percent average or thereabouts in mathematics, physics and chemistry would give me a good chance of winning a county award, but that a seventy percent average or more was needed for a State Scholarship. Consequently we all opted for the county system and geared ourselves to it.

How about personal finances through all this, 'the penny in your pocket' to paraphrase Harold Wilson, who I suppose was working his way towards Oxford at that time, not too far from Bingley, in Huddersfield? We were now mired in the worst years of the great depression. My father had retreated from his business in Bradford, luckily for the family since people who persisted in private business through those years mostly lost their capital. Bankruptcies occurred frequently throughout the whole Aire Valley. Money was therefore tighter for my parents in 1930 than it had been in 1920. Up to the time when I 'matricked', which is to say up to the age of fifteen, I was supported entirely by my parents, with a shilling a week given as pocket money. After matriculation, the West Riding authorities more than made up for any reluctance they'd previously shown over the bus-fare issue by awarding me £15 annually as a contribution to the expenses of further education. It was given as an encouragement to parents to permit their children to remain at school. My own parents reacted with a like generosity by leaving the £15 under my own control. I used it mostly to buy clothes, which perhaps explained why I wasn't knocking my shoes out so much these days by climbing walls. The difference between £15 and the cost of my clothes therefore became the penny in my pocket.

The money had to be watched somewhat carefully, but I don't remember making a big production out of it by fussily keeping detailed accounts. At all times I knew to within a shilling or two what I had, which was entirely sufficient. One extravagance I could not resist was a season ticket to six concerts given in Bradford by the Hallé Orchestra. The bargain offered to pupils in schools throughout the whole Bradford area was simply too good to be missed – six shillings the lot. Fred Jackson and I stumped up our money in good heart for what was to prove one of the best investments of our lives. The return tram fare to Bradford cost sixpence, so it was really one shilling and sixpence per concert. At such a price you might have expected the concert hall to be overflowing with bargain hunters, but I suppose it was known from previous years that this would not be so. Pupils from schools occupied the first three or four rows of the audience, which being almost on top of the orchestra gave us an excellent view of whatever might be going on. Pupils from Bradford Grammar had their seats just in front of ours and it was immediately noticeable to the eye that the girls were not rigorously segregated from the boys, without any suggestion of mayhem breaking loose so far as I could see. Perhaps because it was the first time I'd heard a full orchestra I still remember the programme on that occasion. It had been billed as a symphony concert, and a symphony concert it certainly was: Schubert's 'Unfinished', Sibelius' Symphony Number Two and Beethoven's Fifth. And the conductor? None other than Tommy Beecham himself. It surely was a good bob's worth.

Forty years on, as the Eton Boating Song has it, I attended another performance of Beethoven's Fifth, given at Cornell University by the Baltimore Symphony. As the first movement got under way, I gradually realised from the responses of students around me that many of them had never heard a real live performance of the Fifth before, just as it had been for me so many years earlier. By the mysterious process of communication which undoubtedly exists but which is hard to explain, the sense of excitement in the audience became apparent to the orchestra itself. The players began to work really hard, instead of merely regarding the performance as just another upstate engagement. It was warmish in the hall and I remember the sweat on the musicians' faces as they reached the triumphant coda of the symphony. Beethoven lived in a brief slice of time between the court orchestras of the eighteenth century and orchestras organised by municipal societies in the nineteenth. He gave his own concerts, hiring the musicians and paying them out of his own pocket, which explains why he always made them work hard. He would have enjoyed the sweat on the faces of the Baltimore Symphony, just as he would have enjoyed the regal gestures of Tommy Beecham on the occasion of my own first symphony concert.

The time came at last for the Higher Certificate Examination. My performance was almost exactly as I'd aimed it. By now I'd taken so many tests it had become second nature to judge how well or how badly I'd done with quite a measure of accuracy. On one occasion on my way home in the evening I'd fallen in with E.A.Kaye, the physics master, just after Kaye had finished marking a term examination. Throughout my later years, Kaye and I never ceased trying to take the mickey out of each other.

'How d'you think you've done, position and mark?' he asked.

'Top, with seventy-five percent,' I replied decisively.

'You *are* a conceited blighter, aren't you, Hoyle?' Kaye then said in his not so popular southern accent, adding with a somewhat twisted grin, 'Top, with seventy-six percent.' So I knew I was about right, just OK so far as a Major Scholarship was concerned, but not with any great margin to spare. And I knew, moreover, what I intended to do the coming September. I was entering Leeds University to study chemistry. I would be just past my seventeenth birthday by then, a bit young perhaps, but still consistent with my policy of getting on with the job. I almost had my bags packed, so confident was I that it would work out that way.

And so far as my total score of marks in the examination was concerned, it did work out that way. I was over the average I had aimed for, which in previous years had been considered sufficient for a county scholarship. What I hadn't reckoned with was the 'Geddes Axe'. In response to the mysterious economics of the depression, education budgets were suddenly cut throughout the country. In effect, Yorkshire was asked to close up the gap between its standard and that of the State Scholarships, and I had fallen headlong through the gap.

This was one of the episodes which have convinced me that blows in life, even hard blows – so long as they are not crushing – can be turned to advantage by suitably reorganising oneself. At least it was to prove so, as I shall relate in the next chapter. Momentary episodes of embarrassment in personal relationships have something of the same quality, when just the right words can turn a social disaster into a triumph. The classic example is Samuel Johnson at a dinner with many notables around him, male and female. Deep in conversation, Johnson unwittingly took a very hot potato into his mouth. Immediately and instinctively he spat it openly and volubly back onto his plate. To the startled aristocracy around him, he said: 'A fool would have swallowed that.'

I was too angry to notice an almost pleasing symmetry about my career at Bingley Grammar. I had won my scholarship there in curious circumstances, and I had now been excluded from a leaving scholarship in something like equally unusual circumstances. My overdraft from the Bank of Good Luck, which we all hope to find around the next corner in life, had been repaid.

Chapter Seven

OF THE THREE of us who had worked together, only Edward Foster escaped the Geddes Axe, so it was he who travelled to London in September 1932 to study physics at Imperial College, leaving Fred Jackson and me to return disconsolately to school. I told Alan Smailes, the headmaster, that I was unhappy with the situation. I felt that simply grinding again over the previous year's work might lead to boredom, in which case there would be no guarantee of an improved performance. Smailes took my point, and within a short time he handed me a packet containing the question papers in chemistry, physics and mathematics for the Cambridge scholarship examination which the St John's College group held each year in December. A glance showed them to be in a different league from anything I'd seen before. So far from being able to answer the questions, I didn't even know what most of them meant.

Fred Jackson decided to join in an assault on the same objective, although from September to December 1932 was a pitifully short time to make the upward leap to Cambridge standards. But it is the great advantage of youth that such things do not seem impossible. Fred

Jackson's position was fortunately different from mine in the important respect that the financial position of his parents was better. Fred's father was manager of a branch of Barclays Bank, and he was indeed soon to become manager of the main local headquarters in Bradford. At that time the cost of a Cambridge education was around £200 per annum, and this was not a sum beyond the bounds of possibility for Mr Jackson, especially, I am sure, as Alan Smailes was always seeking to persuade him that Fred should go to Cambridge. Yorkshiremen are canny folk, however, and Mr Jackson wanted to be assured that the extra cost would be worthwhile, and the proof of this was to be in the Cambridge scholarship. Fred's task was therefore to satisfy his father by giving a satisfactory account of himself in the December examination.

It was now at the height of the depression that our chemistry master, Herbert Haigh, bought us books out of his own pocket – and what tremendous books they were. For physical chemistry, we had the classic text of G. N. Lewis. Not that I understood Lewis in any strict sense, but I soon had a general qualitative picture of the various types of chemical bonds. For organic chemistry, our project was little short of fantastic. Lacking substances of appreciable complexity, we began with just two organic compounds, methylated spirits and (I think) benzene. Starting from them, the aim was to synthesize chains of substances, building one on another, rather as one proceeds from proposition to proposition in Euclidean geometry. It was a valid glimpse of the method of operation of the modern chemical industry.

We dug around separately for clues to the answers to the Cambridge questions, pooling our knowledge as we acquired it. Frequently the questions would run us into a brick wall. I still remember struggling vainly to understand the operation of a diffraction grating. At length I asked our physics master, E. A. Kaye, if he could explain.

The answer was short: 'No, I can't, but I can tell you it's difficult.' So far from avoiding the question, Kaye's reply was really a good one. He had taken a first-class himself at Cambridge, in Part I of the Natural Science Tripos. To understand anything of the correct operation of a diffraction grating demands a standard higher even than that. Indeed, the question I had been trying to answer had no business at all to appear in the scholarship examination.

Mathematics was the worst problem, however. Unless one is gifted with exceptional talent, mathematics is difficult to learn alone. Nevertheless, the school had an excellent mathematics teacher. Alan Smailes had been a student at Emmanuel College, where he had taken Part II of the Mathematics Tripos, including the advanced level of what used to be known as 'Schedule B'. Given time, Smailes could have guided us with ease through the Cambridge examination. The trouble was that there was no time. Our own time was short enough, but Smailes himself had little or none. The depths of the great depression was not a period when the education authorities supplied headmasters with secretaries and typists. Smailes had to do every scrap of administration work himself. His days were crammed with minutiae, and the real ability of the best-trained teacher in our school went a-begging.

In this situation, twice a week after dinner, Smailes would have us round to his own house. Although his instruction was entirely unprepared, he would invariably write out the solutions to problems in an unblemished hand. He always went at a slow, methodical pace, excellent for us, digging into his memory as he went along. But it was scarcely enough for us to cope with the meticulously trained products of Britain's specialist schools. Many years later I would myself be an examiner of mathematics papers in the same scholarship group of Cambridge colleges. I found that sets of candidates would tackle questions in precisely the same way, even using identical abstract symbols in their work. For a while I thought there must have been wholesale copying between them. Then I noticed they all belonged to the same school, and had obviously been drilled together like recruits on a parade ground. Against this kind of competition our position in 1932 was extremely weak, but it was a weakness of a somewhat unusual kind. Some things we knew well. But against the things we knew well there were great gaping holes in our knowledge. If we were lucky we might find two or three questions out of ten on a Cambridge mathematics paper which could be summarily dispatched, but the rest would be quite beyond our comprehension.

So the day came in early December 1932 when Fred Jackson and I began our first journey to Cambridge from Bingley Railway Station. In those days you left the local shuttle train at Shipley, where you picked up a connection to Doncaster. There was another change for Peterborough, another for March and Ely, and then a final unhurried link into Cambridge. Fred Jackson and I crowded to the window of the train for our first sight of Cambridge – high spires on the distant horizon. The buildings must have been King's Chapel, John's Chapel, and the Catholic church. A few minutes later we discovered that Cambridge Railway Station is a mile and a half from the town centre, a fact made singular by the unique peculiarity that the 'centre' of Cambridge lies on its circumference. The bus fare changed at Emmanuel College, and as I was going to Emmanuel I paid a penny, whereas Fred who was going to John's paid a penny ha'penny, much to his chagrin.

The Cambridge colleges were mostly empty of their undergraduates during the first week in December, and Emmanuel seemed deserted and forbidding in the fading light of a winter afternoon. It was a curious quirk of psychology that later, when I spent two of my three undergraduate years living in rooms in 'Emma', I could never bring back to memory exactly which rooms I was given on that first occasion. I remember being thoroughly homesick, for this was the first occasion in my seventeen and a half years that I had ever been alone and away from home. I also remember eating dinner in hall for the first time. There was much to amaze me, not least the manner in which some of the regular students who were still in residence made their way in and out of their seats. The tables were wooden, broad and of great length, some arranged parallel and close to the walls. Those who were on the wall side of such tables appeared to be thoroughly wedged in. But not so. At the end of the meal they stood up on their seats, hopped up onto the table and simply marched its length until they could jump down. It seemed that the better-mannered did their best to avoid kicking the plates of those who were still eating.

Such, then, was my background in early December 1932 as I ate dinner that first night at Emmanuel College. I knew nothing then of the parade-ground drilling provided by schools that prided themselves on the achievements of their pupils, schools competing fiercely for the reputation of winning most scholarships at Oxford and Cambridge. Yet I sensed it even on that first night. I listened to the conversation around me, and the gulf between my homespun knowledge and the best from great schools of long experience and tradition was far too obvious to be missed.

It might therefore be supposed that I went along to the first paper – in the hall at John's, I think – in great apprehension. Yet I was entirely relaxed. This Cambridge expedition had not been my idea in the first place. My idea was to become a chemist at Leeds University, and the real problem was to raise my standard to make certain of winning a Yorkshire West Riding scholarship in the summer of 1933. If a miracle happened and I won something in Cambridge, well and good. I would be glad to accept it, but my real aim as I set about answering the first paper was to prove to myself that the efforts of the past three months had really improved my standards.

In this spirit I had a considerable advantage over well-drilled candidates, especially over those who were under pressure to do well. And Cambridge examiners were no easy pushovers for those who only repeated what they had been taught. Every effort was made, as I discovered in later years, to award scholarships to pupils, not to schoolmasters. This was the reason why Cambridge entrance papers contained so many unexpected (and sometimes hopelessly awkward) questions. The aim was to get off the beaten track, so that the examiners could separate spontaneous ability from repetitive efficiency. But of course schoolmasters sometimes became experts themselves at guessing what unbeaten tracks the examiners would choose to follow. Then the unwary examiner could come to believe that he had a genius on his hands. The distinguished mathematician A.S. Besicovitch always believed himself to be discovering genius, and if you happened to be one of Bessi's fellow examiners you risked summary decapitation if you so much as dared suggest that it might not be so.

The chemistry paper fell extremely well for me. The questions in physical chemistry were such that I could throw G.N. Lewis again and again at the examiners, without acknowledgements, I must confess. The physics paper was not quite so good, but tolerable, and the mathematics was just as I had expected. Two or three questions out of ten I could do quickly and well, and then for the rest of the time I tried vainly to guess what the others meant.

There were sessions in practical chemistry and practical physics, the latter held in the old Cavendish Laboratory, and the chemistry in the old Pembroke Street Laboratory. Coming from the tiny cubbyholes at Bingley School, these places seemed vast beyond belief.

The boot was on the other foot now, and with a vengeance. Those who had been carefully trained seemed to know their way around those big laboratories. I knew nothing of laboratory conventions, nothing of where I might expect to find reagents or the simplest equipment. Whenever anything had to be queued for, I always seemed to be the last in line for it.

There was, moreover, a fundamental difficulty. In the theoretical papers the examiners had purposely left their questions a little vague, to give some scope for originality. Practical examinations cannot be left vague, yet the precise specification of what one is expected to do involves technical jargon, and jargon involves conventions. Because I had not been carefully trained in the conventions there were inevitable uncertainties in my mind, semantic uncertainties about exactly what I was expected to do. This difficulty was compounded in the physics practical by certain of the instructions being given verbally, so that I had nothing written down that I could read through several times to clarify the meanings of words. Although I didn't realise it then, the same lack of training in laboratory procedures, and especially a lack of training in keeping laboratory notebooks, had almost certainly cost me a West Riding scholarship the previous summer. We had performed many quite difficult experiments in our cubbyholes, but our style would have been more appropriate to the old alchemists than to these well-scrubbed Cambridge laboratories.

It was while I had something or other 'cooking' in the chemistry practical that a hand tugged at my sleeve and a voice said something in my ear about a chemistry scholarship. I knew nothing about a *chemistry* scholarship. All I knew was that I was seeking what Cambridge called a natural science scholarship. I realised that the hand and voice belonged to a messenger, not to one of the university scientists – you could tell from the smarter suit and the voice. So it would be pointless to ask *what* chemistry scholarship. I simply listened, to learn that I was required to present myself for an oral examination at such and such a place and time.

I noticed the messenger going up to one or two others. Among them was another candidate from Emmanuel, a man called Leben. He was taller than I was, heavier in the shoulders, and he walked with his head thrust a little forward. I had noticed him because, unlike most of the others, he had been quite silent at dinner in the evenings. Of course there were candidates in a wide variety of subjects. Those of us who were 'up' for chemistry, physics and mathematics were, I suppose, about a quarter of the total. There was much cross-talk over the dinner table, not on the first night, but as the examinations proceeded. If all the talk was to be believed, Emmanuel would soon be awarding a powerful lot of scholarships. But of course this was just a way for the candidates to keep up their morale. If they announced to the world how well they had been doing, perhaps some fairy godmother would hear them and it would come true after all.

When the chemistry practical was thankfully over, I asked Leben if he understood this business about a chemistry scholarship. He told me there was to be an award specifically for chemistry, and it must be that the two of us were shortlisted for it. We walked back to Emmanuel together. Later we were to have neighbouring rooms on opposite sides of a staircase of the Drummer Street hostel, with Geoffrey Jackson, the ex-British Ambassador to Uruguay, two doors away from us. I turned up for the chemistry oral at the appointed time. It was in Emmanuel too. I went up the appropriate staircase and knocked at the appropriate numbered room. There was a shout and I went in.

I was not to get that chemistry scholarship, but I can scarcely complain at the competence of the man who now sat facing me as I stood awkwardly before him, since thirty years or so later the man would receive a Nobel Prize for Chemistry, something which even he could not guess, because the work for which the prize was to be awarded still lay far in the future. Nor could I guess that the day would come when I would be Ron Norrish's guest when he was President of the Savage Club. The Savage Club does not provide its President with a toy of a gavel. It furnishes him with a massive knobkerrie that could smash your skull as easily as a hen's egg. My overwhelming memory of Norrish is of the smile on his face as he pounded furiously with that lethal instrument in prelude to the speech I was to make. The thunder of it still rings in my ears, quite excluding all efforts to recall just what happened during the oral examination back in 1932. I could never get Norrish himself to remember the occasion, and I myself remember only a single odd detail. It had never occurred to me that the word 'halogen' could be pronounced with anything but a short 'a'. Norrish pronounced it hale-ogen, astonishing me mightily, although I would not wish to claim that it was my bemusement on this matter which cost me the chemistry scholarship.

Cambridge did not keep either its own undergraduates or its scholarship candidates on tenterhooks for very long. Within not much more than a week of my return home to Bingley, I had a letter from Emmanuel giving highly detailed marks of my performances. In total I was a mere handful below what was called 'exhibition standard', which was the lowest level at which Cambridge awarded money. My theoretical paper in chemistry had been of scholarship standard, but I had of course been pulled down by the practical test; but in total I was still above exhibition standard for chemistry. Likewise in physics I was just above exhibition standard. It was mathematics which pulled the whole thing down below this apparently mythical standard. The few questions in mathematics I had understood and answered had given me solid marks, but they were just too few to maintain the standard.

Thinking I had lost only £40 a year, which was the extent of an exhibition award and which would not have taken me to Cambridge anyway, I went to see Alan Smailes and showed him the letter. As he read it through he came as near swearing in real anger as I had ever observed him. Only then did he explain what that standard would have meant, and what those few missed marks had cost me. The point was not the £40. The point was that *if* I had obtained the standard, and *if* I should obtain a West Riding scholarship in the coming summer, then Yorkshire would have met all my Cambridge expenses. Without the mythical standard, they would not do so. Like the axing of scholarships the previous summer, it was another of fate's minor digs in the ribs.

I made my way to the public library in the centre of Bingley and found there the copy of *The Times* with the 'John's group' scholarship results in it. As my eye travelled down the list of awards, I saw that Leben had won the special chemistry scholarship, and in that moment I found that I envied him. It was with this momentary surge of emotion that for the first time I realised that I wanted to go to Cambridge.

Left to myself I would have been beaten, but Alan Smailes was not. He soon discovered that Pembroke College held its scholarship examinations in March. The situation could be recovered, he told me, if I were to attain the standard there. So the pressure was on. I knew the stake now, and I had three months more to force the position.

Oddly, I remember very little of that second attempt. Nothing of the train journey, which I made alone since Fred Jackson's father had been happy to accept his entry to St John's. I remember nothing of the dinners, only of the room I was allotted – not of its interior, but of a climb up a long flight of stone stairs to reach it. I knew nothing then of the great ghosts who walk the cloisters of Pembroke – of James Clerk Maxwell from Edinburgh, or George Gabriel Stokes from County Sligo. I do not even remember the details of the written examination itself, only that my performance was somewhat less brittle than it had been in December.

I have just one clear memory – of another oral examination to which I was called, this time in physics. I do not know if I was called because I was a contender for some award. If so, I didn't get it. The examiner was Philip Dee. Later I discovered that Dee had something of a reputation for giving students a hard time, and he quite certainly gave me a hard time. When I was seeking to answer a question on absolute temperatures he got me in something of a tangle and then exclaimed: 'Is there *any* physics you *do* know?'

This was the sort of remark which gets me fighting mad, and instantly I dumped my deferential attitude and waded into Dee just as hard as I could. As with Norrish, I was never able later to get him to remember the occasion. He had no recall of the broad-spoken candidate from Yorkshire who had sparked back at him. I had been but a momentary irritation, an unwelcome interruption from some more important activity: 'Glad to have finished with these damned scholarship candidates,' was a remark I was to hear often at High Table in later years.

In spite of this encounter with Philip Dee I travelled back to Yorkshire with cautious optimism. There was no letter from Pembroke setting out my results in detail as Emmanuel had done. There was simply a short communication, regretting that I had not been given an award. Smailes wrote off in great anxiety about the elusive standard. Soon there was a further reply, saying that it gave the tutor at Pembroke pleasure to report that I had indeed attained the exhibition standard. This can happen even though there is no actual award, because there are often more candidates above the standard than there are awards available. Yet since I never saw the actual marks, I do not know to this day what the situation really was. A kind-hearted tutor might quite well have given Smailes the answer he so obviously wanted, since it cost the college no money to do so. If so, the kind-hearted tutor made a profound difference to my life.

But all this would be a pointless charade unless I should win the West Riding scholarship, which by now Smailes and my parents seemed to be taking for granted. The Higher Certificate examinations started in late June, when circumstances fell out that my parents and young sister had a chance of a holiday in Cornwall. But the period of the holiday would overlap with the two-week duration of the examinations, and my mother would not hear of being away at such a critical time. I made strenuous protestations that the opportunity should not be missed – holidays that could be afforded, as this one could, were scarce in our family. And if the truth were told, I was not unhappy at the thought of our small house being quiet when I needed it to be quiet. Still more important, there would be no one to offer consolation and advice if I should happen to hit a bad paper. Too much solicitude leads inevitably to a crack-up, with worse to follow.

I had no bad papers that summer and I obtained the Yorkshire scholarship by a safe margin. Yet fate still could not quite let me off its hook. With six months' further experience after reaching scholarship standard in chemistry at Cambridge, I might have been expected to run away with the chemistry paper, and this is exactly what I thought I had done. I did not seem to find a difficulty anywhere, and the questions with definite answers had all been verified later – the answers I had written on the margin of the printed question papers were correct. Yet my marks were completely the reverse of the Cambridge results. In mathematics my percentage was up in the eighties, in physics in the upper seventies, and in chemistry down just below the seventy level. From 1930 to 1933, I sat four chemistry examinations set by the Northern Matriculation Board, and each time my result was about fifteen percentage points lower than I expected it to be. Once or perhaps twice I might have misjudged the situation, but not, I think, four times. There had to be something wrong for the Northern Board examiners about my style, and something right about it for the Cambridge examiners. The Northern examiners apparently did not want G. N. Lewis – evidently they had little use for differences between chemical bondings. The year being 1933, only eight years after the beginnings of modern quantum theory, and hence of modern chemistry, such matters were probably too new. What the devil the Northern Board really did want I never discovered, for nobody could tell me. Perhaps it was carefully drawn, ruled diagrams, instead of my freely and rather badly rendered sketches. The situation was interesting because of what it revealed about the vicissitudes to which youngsters are exposed, even in an apparently strict science. The vicissitudes of examiners must be greater in history, economics and English literature, and they could even be important in mathematics – if A. S. Besicovitch happened to be around, although Bessi's vicissitudes were sharply in the upward direction, never downwards.

There is no doubt at all that it was much harder for students dependent on scholarships to gain access to universities in my time than it is today, and that the situation in this respect was particularly severe in the early thirties. But there was now a big compensation. It would be unheard of today for a student, completing his financing as late as September, to enter a Cambridge college less than a month later. Nowadays entry would inevitably be delayed a further year. But the pressure on the colleges was less in 1933, and now my marks at the

December examination stood strongly to my advantage. Emmanuel wanted me, because for a 'commoner' rather than a 'scholar' my standard was quite good. Besides which, I am sure the letters written by Alan Smailes to his old college had maintained a stubborn vagueness about my prospective finances, to such an extent that the college had been persuaded to keep a place open for me.

So it came about that at the beginning of October 1933 I journeyed again to Cambridge, again by train, changing at Shipley, Doncaster, etc, and again in the company of Fred Jackson. We parted company at Cambridge Railway Station. In the months ahead we were to see each other only occasionally, for the logistic reason that our 'digs' were widely separated on opposite sides of town. His were situated in a maze of streets to the north of Chesterton Road, and mine were far south, close to where the railway bridge crosses Mill Road. There was no thought at all of our hiring taxis at the station, as I was to do so often in later years. Fred took the bus, paying twopence, I suppose, to Chesterton Road, while I humped my heavy suitcase the half-mile into Mill Road. The route was unfamiliar to me, and I remember twice asking the way.

One of the first things to be done was to have a personal interview with one's college tutor. This does not necessarily mean one's teacher or 'supervisor'. A tutor's job is to look after an undergraduate's worldly well-being, like bailing him out of jail. It is perfectly possible for a science student to have a historian or a classics don as tutor, although by and large an attempt is made to minimise such big differences. Thus although I was a science student, apparently destined to work for the Natural Science Tripos, my tutor was a mathematician.

P. W. Wood was a striking and tragic Cambridge figure. He was tallish, quite thin, with a slight stoop. He mostly walked around the room as he talked, likely enough jangling keys in his pocket. He had a big beak of a nose through which he sniffed frequently and very audibly. He wore casual 'bags' and a tweed jacket liberally studded with leather patches. These leather patches were a kind of badge of the Cambridge don. You could always distinguish them from the servants, who were more neatly dressed in dark suits.

At the risk of incurring the scorn of mathematicians more profound than I am, I have no hesitation in saying that P.W. was the finest Cambridge geometer of his generation. The trouble lay in his style of geometry. Nowadays mathematicians use an algebraic style just as Wood did, but in Cambridge up to 1939 the preferred style was different: almost everything was argued in words, which was really a negation of mathematics, for one of the most powerful weapons of mathematics lies in its notations, and the preferred style of Cambridge geometry (whose protagonists referred to themselves as 'pure' geometers) made little or no use of notations.

P.W. Wood, on the other hand, was an outstanding master of notation, a breathtaking wizard at it. He would begin by writing a seemingly straightforward equation on the blackboard. Now came the tour of the lecture room, talking the whole while with head down and keys jangling. When the tour reached the blackboard again he would add some apparently simple superscript or subscript to the symbols in his equation, which he did casually as he passed by. The tour would be repeated, with a further casual addition to the equation at the second passage by the board. And now at the third tour the real sniffing would begin, so that you knew the denouement to be fast approaching. On reaching the blackboard yet again he would delicately adjust his subscripts and superscripts, the notation, and lo and behold the proof of some startling proposition, which you might have puzzled about all morning without being able to prove, was suddenly before your eyes. It was characteristic of P.W.'s marvellous sleight of hand that you were always convinced at the moment of revelation that you could perform the same rabbit-out-of-a-hat trick for yourself, but when a couple of hours later you tried you couldn't. Nor, I think, could P.W.'s fellow geometers, and this was exactly why they condemned his methods.

The Cambridge fad for 'pure' geometry, or 'projective' geometry as it is more properly called, had been given impetus earlier in the century by H.F. Baker, whose several unreadable volumes on the subject I still keep on my shelves to remind me of how far a fad can go. There is a damaging modern fad abroad in physics and engineering which goes by the name of the S.I. System. A book entitled *S.I. Units, a System for Fools*, which I wrote some years ago, still lacks a publisher. Indeed, whenever I mention it, publishers always show me the door. This too was poor P.W.'s position. Nobody would take him seriously, except a yearly sprinkling of discerning students. Wood had really only himself to blame, I suppose. He was at the height of his powers at just the time Einstein published his general theory of relativity. Instead of continuing to fight a worthless battle with H.F. Baker, he should have transferred his interests to Riemannian geometry and general relativity. If he had done so, his impact would quite likely have been sensational. It was similar unfortunate judgements, allied to a sharp tongue, which caused him to be passed over several times for the Mastership of Emmanuel.

My last memories of Wood are from the autumn of 1945. I had just been made a junior lecturer at Cambridge and my first task was to give a course of lectures in geometry to science students. The number of students was so large that it was necessary for the course to be given in parallel by two lecturers (in different rooms of course). The other lecturer was P.W. I had been away from Cambridge from 1940 until the early summer of

1945 and so had not seen him for some time. He was on the verge of retirement now, looking older than he really was, more stooping and thinner than before. I walked into the lecturers' common room to find him already there, walking around in the same characteristic pose, head down, keys jangling. As I came in he looked up with the wry twist to the corners of his lips that was the nearest I ever saw P.W. come to a smile. Eyeing me ironically, he said: 'Well, Hoyle, we meet again under changed circumstances.'

Indeed it was then a far cry back to the day, almost exactly twelve years before, when I first called on P.W. Wood. After turning in at the front gate of Emmanuel you took the staircase immediately on the left. P.W.'s rooms were one flight up. I knocked, waited for the shout, and then went in. P.W. didn't waste any words. From a file, he took a sheet which showed my marks from the December scholarship exam. He studied it with a loud, disconcerting sniff. I waited in silence until the process was complete. At length he said: 'Not good in mathematics. Not good enough for a real scientist.' I was tempted to blurt out that my recent Higher Certificate performance was better, but then I reflected that Alan Smailes must certainly have written about the Higher Certificate results. So I asked what would he, P.W., do about it? 'You might consider Mathematics, Part I,' he replied.

In a few tersely worded sentences he told me that the first part of the Mathematics Tripos was a one-year course, and this would leave me favourably placed with two years to devote to Natural Sciences Part II, instead of the usual one year, which was much too short for effective specialisation in either physics or chemistry. He told me that in any case I must already have covered a fair portion of the first-year chemistry and physics, and that if I opted immediately for science I would spend most of my time studying subjects I didn't really wish to do, such as botany or geology. 'Go away and think about it,' he concluded.

Two days later I returned and told P.W. I would accept his advice, whereon he sniffed and said that it wasn't advice he offered, only the facts of Cambridge life. Neither of us thought it a particularly important decision. For me, however, it was to be a watershed. It was to lead, not to a leisurely two years of chemistry or physics as we both thought then, but to the full rigours of the later parts of the Mathematical Tripos. I was either too late or too incapable ever to become a creative mathematician, but the training I would receive in the next three years would have one inestimable value. When I eventually returned to science, it would be with a thoroughly sound mathematical technique. It was the real beginning.

Chapter Eight

MATHEMATICS HAD always been the jewel in the Cambridge academic crown. In the good old days you had to acquit yourself first in mathematics before you were permitted to proceed to other subjects of study. Students in mathematics in 1933 constituted about ten percent of the whole university, with an intake of about 150 new faces each year, divided into two roughly equal streams – a fast stream and a slow stream, taking different examinations and attending different lectures. In effect, the slow stream was one year behind the fast stream, with the fast stream made up about half-and-half of exceptionally gifted students for whom Cambridge was their first university, aged about the same as me, and a considerably older group who had already completed a first-class degree at some other university, British and Commonwealth, and who then came to Cambridge for a final topping-up. In particular there had always been a strong intake from Scottish universities. Because they had already received a good quality training, not quite up to the Cambridge level but not too far short of the first two years' work, these advanced students from Scotland always scored very well in the Mathematics Tripos.

Even this powerful contingent of older students from other universities did not represent the ultimate pinnacle of the competition, however. At the very summit were dazzlingly able students who showed their ability immediately, without needing to pass through another university. These were the ones who appeared at the top of the Cambridge scholarships, not the scholarships in Natural Sciences I described in the previous chapter, but in Mathematics itself. Mostly the bigger colleges, Trinity especially, grabbed these nuggets of gold straight from school. Such a one was a friend of later years, who was starting his last year as an undergraduate at the time in 1933 when I was just beginning. With respect to the problems which constituted a mathematics examination, it was said of Maurice Pryce that every time he looked at the question paper you knew he'd done another one, which was surely depressing for the other candidates who happened to be sitting near him.

The most awesome piece of mathematical virtuosity I ever saw was done by Pryce. It happened in around 1941 in the following circumstances. As you go further and further away from a radio transmitter the direct signal from the transmitter weakens. The calculation of how the signal weakens with distance is quite easy so long as the transmitter remains in view, but the calculation becomes increasingly awkward as you pass more and more over the horizon. Indeed with the method formerly used, long and tedious calculations were needed to determine the answer for even a single over-the-horizon case. So what, you might ask? Well, in 1940–41 the Germans had a scheme for guiding their night bombers using intersecting radio beams from two such over-the-horizon transmitters. They destroyed the centre of Coventry with it, and fear instantly erupted that the same would happen in every English city. R. V. Jones describes in his book *Most Secret War* the ensuing political panic at the highest level of government, with nobody able to say just how far the Germans would be able to go. Jones tells how it became a critical question of whether the signals from the German transmitters would extend as far as Wolverhampton. He blames the BBC engineers who were consulted for giving equivocal and sometimes misleading answers, but this I think may not be quite fair, because before Pryce's solution of the problem nobody could give reliable answers without long and intensive calculations.

What Pryce set himself to do was to rework the mathematics so that answers to such questions as those which tied the government in knots during the 'Battle of the Beams' could be given in only a few minutes. He did so not from a don's pleasant rooms overlooking Great Square in Trinity, but from a small, harshly furnished office, shared with two others and with telephones ringing perpetually, in a building in war-torn Portsmouth where bombing raids occurred pretty well every night. I was working at a country out-station at the time. One day I received a telephone call from Pryce, telling me what he had done and asking if I would be willing to check the details for him. We arranged to meet and Maurice handed me about a dozen sheets of white unlined paper, not quite as large as the student pads we bought from Heffers' shop in Cambridge. Everything was there in remorselessly logical sequence, set out in neat handwriting.

Why is it, one wonders, that the ablest people always seem to be the neatest? A friend who has studied Mozart's manuscripts told me Mozart always wrote the notes down beautifully, even as the music came out of his head for the first time. Except on one occasion, my friend said, when Mozart crossed the waltz with the minuet in the ballroom scene of *Don Giovanni* and things didn't work out on paper quite as he'd expected. So, my friend added: 'There were crossings-out, just like the rest of us.' Luckily for Maurice Pryce he never tried to cross a waltz and a minuet, at least not to my knowledge.

I think it is correct to say the staff of the Mathematics Faculty in Cambridge was overwhelmingly the most powerful of any British university. In 1933 there were five professors in the faculty together with something approaching thirty lecturers, many of the lecturers in addition to the professors being Fellows of the Royal Society. Cambridge mathematics was a lodestone for the majority of mathematically able students throughout the United Kingdom, and indeed for some far beyond that. If one sets the catchment population yielding the annual intake of 150 students as thirty millions, the estimate would, I think, be conservative. It would give an average production rate of one student per 200,000 population per year. For the best ten students, on the other hand, the production rate would be one per three million population per year, while for the outstandingly best like Maurice Pryce it would be one per thirty million population per year. Remembering that the production rate in those days for Fellows of the Royal Society was one per four million per year, it could easily be predicted that, except for those who deliberately left the mathematical field – for example to enter the Civil Service, the best few each year would inevitably be elected to the Royal Society, a prediction that generally speaking proved to be verified in later years. And with really exceptional students like Maurice Pryce the Society might perhaps have elected him in 1931 rather than waiting until 1951. You can't beat the percentages, as they say in baseball.

I could not claim myself to be one of the average mathematics students in the one in 200,000 class, since I came to mathematics because I was weak in it. In chemistry or physics I might reasonably be said to have demonstrated this kind of an average standard, but my mathematics in October 1933 was evidently at a statistically lower level. My entry point into Cambridge mathematics was, therefore, at the bottom of the slow stream, and the question in my first year as an undergraduate was whether I could manage to come up to speed with the slow stream. This was the challenge my tutor P. W. Wood had set for me.

In later years I became an examiner myself in the various parts of the Mathematical Tripos, so I had eventual access to the examiners' mark books. Such information is, I suppose, confidential, strictly speaking, but I see no profound objection to saying what my performances were, provided I say nothing about anyone else's. In the examination held at the end of the first year in May 1934 I was three-quarters of the way up the list from the bottom, or a quarter of the way down from the top, according to how you prefer to look at it. In effect, I had come up to speed with the slow stream, and it was time for me now to return to physics and chemistry, as I had planned with my tutor at the beginning of the year.

Inevitably, however, the entire style of my educational history prompted the question: if I were to stay in mathematics, how far in the next two years could I catch up with the leaders? To have any chance of moving towards the front of the field I would evidently need to leap immediately across from the slow stream to the fast stream, which meant jumping a whole year all in one gulp. At the level of Cambridge mathematics, that would be a far greater feat than the jump of a year I'd made at school in my matriculation year. Besides, wasn't physics my real line, not mathematics? Yet could I really return to physics without feeling I'd ducked a challenge? These were the questions that filled my mind over the summer of 1934.

I remarked in an earlier chapter how from Rombald's Moor, which could be seen, it will be recalled, from the windows of my home, it was possible to walk almost the whole way to Edinburgh without passing anything more populated than remote farmhouses and hamlets. In my later years at school I had begun to explore the vastness of the territory which had lain so long on my doorstep. Now in the summer of 1934 I penetrated much further into the wild country. Together with Fred Jackson and Edward Foster, I made an extensive walking tour of the North Yorkshire Dales. Then came two tours of the Lake District with Edward Foster. These hill-walking trips provided ideal circumstances in which to mull over the choices before me.

Although we lived economically in youth hostels during our walking trips, the total cost ran to perhaps £10, and a question naturally arises of where a sum of that magnitude came from, especially as there was also excess wear and tear on clothes to be considered. My grant of £225 per year from the West Riding of Yorkshire was nicely tailored to include lecture fees, which were very modest, college fees, which were not quite so modest, food and lodgings, clothes, and subscriptions to those university and college clubs to which an undergraduate might normally expect to belong. The latter, such as the Cambridge Union, were not obligatory, however. Since the Yorkshire authorities simply made a flat grant without calling for detailed accounting, I had a free choice of whether I would plump for the optional extras, so running my finances essentially to zero, or whether I would forego the extras in the interest of establishing an annual contingency of about £25. In October 1933 I chose the latter course, and very glad I eventually became that I had done so. The money for the walking tours came from my contingency, while in the university itself there proved to be worthwhile activities I could not have noticed at the beginning, which I would have been precluded from joining had I consumed all my resources at the outset. Shortly after my first visit to the University Chess Club I was asked to become a member of the university team. Over the winter of 1933–4 the cost of travel to away matches was about £5. One of the away matches happened to be with the House of Commons, so permitting me an intimate sight of the Mother of Parliaments I couldn't easily have obtained otherwise. And at a later date I joined a rambling club which was to establish lifelong friendships of considerable significance. While the expenditures involved there were but a few pounds, even such sums are decisively inhibitory if you are entirely out of funds. So although I had to forego some of the standard attractions of undergraduate life, my fiscal policy proved wise.

As I walked the Yorkshire Dales and the mountains of the Lake District in July and August 1934, the decision I had to make came to seem less difficult than it had done in Cambridge. A decision in October 1934 to join the fast stream in mathematics would not be irreversible, because up to Easter 1935 I could always go back to the slow stream. What was irreversible was a decision between mathematics and physics. If by mathematics one had meant mathematics in a European or American sense, my choice would undoubtedly have been physics. But mathematics in Cambridge included what elsewhere was called theoretical physics. The choice in essence, therefore, lay between theoretical and experimental physics. If I stayed with mathematics I could evolve eventually into theoretical physics, but if I wished to become an experimental physicist I must return to the laboratories without delay. Which way did I wish to go? My choice, I came to feel, was decided by history, by the fact that probably the major fraction of outstanding Cambridge physicists had evolved through mathematics – Newton, of course, Maxwell, Kelvin, Thompson, Cockroft, Eddington and Dirac. This seemed decisive, so mathematics it was.

With the principle of the matter thus settled, I argued on my return to Cambridge for my second undergraduate year in October 1934 that the situation was not too much different from the previous year. I was now at the bottom of the fast stream instead of the bottom of the slow stream. If I could work my position, by the time of the next examination in May 1935, three-quarters of the way up from the bottom, or a quarter of the way down from the top, according to the way you care to look at it, I could reckon I had come satisfactorily up to speed. This, then, was my objective for the second year.

In the event I did not succeed. In the examination of May 1935 I came three-fifths of the way up the fast stream. This, however, was the examination in which I had the bad migraine headache I mentioned in an earlier chapter. It occurred on the very last paper, just as I was beginning to feel I'd attained my objective. Just as with the attack of mumps on the occasion of my junior scholarship, I felt there was no point in making a public issue of the matter. Surely but for the migraine, I told myself, I would have scored better on that last paper, and so psychologically if not objectively I counted my real position a little higher, perhaps even approaching the objective I'd set. At all events, I could plainly see now the leaders ahead of me on the running track. For the first time I had a really clear aim – to spurt in my final year into the top ten, because, of course, it was the top ten who would receive further grants to continue in research if they so wished.

Through June and July 1935 I gave attention to the kind of work I would do in the final year. It was on a bigger scale than before, more like playing a whole sonata instead of concentrating on student exercises. I became generally hopeful that the bigger scale would suit me, and that the individualistic aspects of my early education might now at last become an advantage.

Together with Edward Foster I took off in August on another walking tour. Edward had just finished his normal three undergraduate years, and he was mighty pleased to have secured a grant that permitted him to continue further at Imperial College, as I recall in vacuum spectroscopy. I hoped the next year I would be able to say the same. Instead of confining ourselves to week-long tours, we were six weeks in the Scottish Highlands. At the end I was considerably fitter and stronger than I'd ever been before, and it was in this condition that I journeyed to Cambridge in early October 1935.

Lectures were attended now by research students as well as undergraduates. Imperceptibly as time went on I came more into contact with research students than with my fellow undergraduates. The process was greatly aided by my joining the rambling club I mentioned earlier. I did so initially to maintain something of the fitness I'd acquired in the Scottish Highlands, but there I made firm and lasting friendships, particularly with several of the ramblers who were research students. Through them, especially through George Carson, a biologist, and Charles (E.T.) Goodwin, a theoretical physicist, I came to know still more of the research students. Charles Goodwin had come through the Mathematical Tripos himself, just as I was doing, and so there was much to talk about.

The rambling club went far outside Cambridge each Sunday, usually some thirty miles in a hired bus from Drummer Street, immediately behind my rooms in the Emmanuel College hostel. We brought our own sandwiches and would eat them in a village pub somewhere in the wilds. The main business of the day was then to walk for perhaps three hours along small paths and often across ploughed fields thick with soft clay. To obviate arguments over the route, a 'leader' chosen in advance was supposed to have been over the route previously to ensure that we didn't end up in the wrong place on a short winter afternoon, the 'right place' being the spot where our hired bus had been instructed to meet us. The right place was also some pub, inn, or café where an excellent tea was to be had by one and all. After returning to

Cambridge we took a bath and ate dinner individually, meeting afterwards for coffee in the rooms of the club's founder, Harry Marshall. Harry was the only one of my Cambridge friends to die in the Second World War. He entered the Foreign Service and was sent to Malaya in 1937. I was told he was upstate at the time of the Japanese invasion from the north in early 1942. Although not trained as a soldier, he volunteered for a holding operation and was not seen again.

As the year 1935–6 progressed, I never lost the fitness I'd acquired in the Scottish Highlands. Indeed from Easter onwards, instead of retreating into my books as in former years, the amount of outdoor activity increased still more. As well as the Sunday walks, I would often go canoeing on weekdays with Charles Goodwin and George Carson. We were emphatic in preferring a heavy wooden affair, which we hired on a long-term basis from a boathouse just below Magdalene Bridge, to the lightweight jobs that rode higher and higher as they picked up speed, making it impossible to get what we considered a satisfactory bite from the paddles. The paddles were one-sided with handles. Eventually there became only one possible arrangement – Charles Goodwin in the front on the left, myself in the middle paddling on the right, and George Carson in the guiding spot at the rear, paddling either side according to the expediencies of the moment. You grasped the cross-piece at the end of the paddle with one hand and delivered the stroke with that hand and corresponding shoulder, the other hand beginning each stroke firmly holding the paddle shaft immediately above the blade. At the last moment you had to whip your lower thumb away from the shaft to avoid it being crushed against the side of the boat. The problem was to get our timing co-ordinated with the strongest strokes we could manage and without ruining the lower thumb and fingers. From that time in 1936 through two consecutive summers until Charles

Goodwin left Cambridge, we prided ourselves on being the fastest craft afloat on the River Cam. I can't be certain we were, but I can say that nobody ever beat us in a challenge. Our time from Byron's Pool to the Garden House Hotel became incredibly short.

This might seem a strange way to prepare for the most important examination of one's life. But as the year had progressed I had become steadily more confident. The curious aspect of it was that in my very last examination of all I had begun to appreciate how it would have felt to have been a golden boy, if only it had fallen out that way earlier in my career. What had actually happened by May 1936 was that I'd once again exercised my penchant for jumping. My acquaintances and friends were all now research students, so that, so long as pride did not go before a fall in the examination itself, I had jumped entirely out of my own year.

Lectures for the final part of the Mathematical Tripos had finished now, but there were still special courses organised for research students. Together with Charles Goodwin I attended two of them, one given by Rudolf Peierls and the other by Max Born, both on quantum field theory. Born lectured on Monday, the day after the walks of the Sunday rambling club. One Sunday a dozen or so of us had decided on a whim to walk forty miles. We started early from Cambridge. Instead of taking a bus in the usual way, we walked from the city centre out along the Roman Road as far as Haverhill, where we had lunch. In the afternoon my rucksack seemed unduly heavy, until I discovered it to contain stones, put there, as I recall, by a friend who was a printer's son from York, Bill Sessions. We joined the rest of the club for tea with the best part of thirty miles behind us. After tea we did the last ten miles back to Cambridge, with Charles Goodwin and I accelerating over the last three miles because we didn't want to miss a performance on the radio that night of Beethoven's Emperor Concerto. We just had time for a bath at Charles' digs in Station Road before the music came on. Then, after a meal with Charles, I stumbled in a thoroughly stiff condition from Station Road back to Emmanuel College.

In these days of widespread media coverage we hear of lots of people walking fantastically big distances. Such people must be exceptional. There are very few indeed who can walk big distances without ill effects, and these few are mostly small or thin people with comparatively light impact forces on the feet. We were quite fit young people at the prime of life, but I think only one of us, a girl, suffered no noticeable ill effects from our forty-mile walk. Bill Sessions was a big man, very springy on his feet, and in winter he was the goalkeeper for a well-known amateur soccer club. Bill suffered badly in the final stages of that walk, and it was some revenge for the stones in my rucksack when, in the final miles, I could hear him muttering, 'What does a ghost care about its feet?'

The following day I had quite seized up, and because of the slowness of my walk I was late at Max Born's lecture. He had not started yet, but was just on the point of doing so when I appeared. Let me draw the picture. My academic gown I had bought second-hand for thirty pence at the beginning of my undergraduate life in 1933, and while it did not have the savagely ripped appearance of the gowns of the young bloods about town it had very definitely seen better days. In the matter of shirts, this was about the time when several of us found that Selfridge's in Oxford Street had a line of them going at twopence ha'penny each. We bought a pile with the idea of giving each one a thoroughly good wear, and then simply chucking 'em out to avoid laundry expenses. It was the idea of the disposable razor, but in 1936 it was an idea before its time.

Shoes were an impossibility for me that day – I was reduced to wearing a hastily borrowed ancient pair of gym shoes, one of them without a lace. In addition to all this, I couldn't walk properly. The best I could do was to sort of drag myself across the small lecture room, immediately past the lectern where Max Born was standing. Afterwards Maurice Blackman, later Professor of Physics at Imperial College, said with a big grin: 'It wasn't like that for Born in Germany. He was as near as dammit to hoofing you out.' This was as near as I ever came to exchanging a word with Max Born.

The two weeks before the examination I spent the mornings working and the afternoons on the river. The week of the Mathematical Tripos was exceedingly hot in 1936. The heat was an advantage, however. Being exceptionally fit now, I felt no oppression or heaviness in the head, as I would have done the previous year, and the warmth allowed me to write quickly for long periods. After the two papers on the first day, I joined George Carson for tea in one of the town cafés. To his enquiry, I committed myself as far as to say I thought I'd done reasonably good papers.

The final undergraduate year was different from the previous two in the important respect that one expected to receive the BA at the Degree Day ceremony held in the fourth week of June. This left a three-week period between the end of examinations and the ceremony itself. Not wanting to kick our heels around Cambridge over these three weeks, a party of us decided on a hitch-hiking trip to Cornwall. Hitch-hiking was a new idea at that time, and it had been imported into Cambridge from the United States by Ivan Inksetter, a very tall, thin fellow.

Inksetter's christian name was not Ivan. He came by his pseudonym through a misguided attempt to row in the low echelons of the Lady Margaret Boat Club. The story was that one day the Captain of Boats caught sight of Inksetter at work. Stopping dead in his tracks, the Captain exclaimed, 'God, who's that, Ivan the Terrible?' So Inksetter became Ivan throughout Cambridge. I never knew his real christian name. He was a student in English, and so had natural entry to the Marlowe Society, the undergraduate theatrical group. Probably he is the only member of the Marlowe Society ever to have caused a sensation from the stage without speaking a word – as the corpse in an Aristophanes comedy.

Before setting out for Cornwall, I went to see Rudolf Peierls in his office in the Mond Laboratory to ask if he would agree to be my supervisor should I be able to obtain a research grant. Peierls said he would consider the matter. I learned afterwards that he had subsequently enquired around Cambridge to find out who I was, but nobody knew. Particularly, I had not applied for a research studentship from the Department of Scientific and Industrial Research (DSIR). The trouble with those studentships was that you had to apply for an award at Easter time, two months or so before the examination, which seemed an obvious invitation to providence to hit me with another migraine or with a refurbished Geddes Axe. It was now too late to obtain a DSIR studentship, no matter what the result of the examination might be, since in those days there was no late appeals system such as has been set up in more recent years. If you didn't apply in April, you couldn't get a studentship. My ace in the hole, however, was that the West Riding of Yorkshire had provision for the continuation of their scholarships over a further year, in 'exceptional circumstances'. A good result in the examination would, I knew, be construed as an exceptional circumstance.

Even this final contretemps, involving the apparently considerable risk that after my first year of research I would find myself without support, turned out an advantage. My contemporaries who were awarded DSIR studentships were required, as you might expect from anything connected with bureaucracy or government, to write terminal progress reports. Because I became favoured with a more aristocratic style of support, I did not have to follow this procedure. I was able to go as I liked, and since it transpired that the best way to go seemed to be on my own, I was able to cut myself free at last. The bureaucracy would never have permitted me thus to stand on my own feet, which being unusual was against the rules. To satisfy bureaucracy you had to be everlastingly subjected to instruction, which is why science today, being almost entirely controlled by bureaucracy, is a mostly unproductive activity.

I had not hitch-hiked before. There were many fewer cars on the roads in those days, often almost none on the small roads. But a far higher proportion of motorists would give you a lift than will do so today. Ivan Inksetter and I had finished our examinations ahead of the others, and we set out for Cornwall a week earlier. Inksetter was the original master hitch-hiker. He dressed for the part. Very tall and thin as I have said, he was wearing shorts, a Tyrolean hat with feathers in it and a jacket of the same vintage with bells and big silver-looking buttons on its front. Few cars, when we wanted one, ever passed us by on that trip.

Inksetter was highly skilled at choosing his cars. In poor districts, like the mining districts of Cornwall, he was happy enough to tuck his long legs into a small Ford. But in wealthy areas he had a quick eye for the Bentleys and Rolls-Royces, being especially fond of the latter. It was, as I recall, in the region of Ascot on the very first day out of Cambridge that Inksetter landed an exceptional ride. The lady owner of the Rolls-Royce invited us to tea at some large estate, where we were served tiny sandwiches on a silver salver by a butler in tails. Although hungry, since we had foregone lunch, I remember thinking that as the sandwiches were scarcely worth eating in a nutritive sense I could afford to be conspicuously polite by eating them very slowly.

The situation was distinctly horsey, a topic on which I have never at any time excelled, since I have always agreed with the man who said: 'I know before it starts that a horse race is going to be won by a horse, and I don't much care which.' This view not being popular on that occasion, I had to leave the burden of conversation to Ivan Inksetter. He had a big, resonant bass voice, and I think he really enjoyed the situation, blarneying his way through it. We ended our first day out of Cambridge at a youth hostel in Winchester. Being exceedingly hungry by now, we consumed a mixed grill for 1*s* 3*d* in a café, not so politely, with thick slices of bread and butter.

It was my first visit to Devon and Cornwall. The second day we reached a youth hostel at Dunsford, a country village about half-way between Exeter and Moretonhamstead. The third day we were in the region of St Austell. Thereafter we moved around the Cornish coast. We had no preconceptions about what to expect, and it was with profound surprise and delight that we came to the coastline between Newquay and Padstow, hitting it at just about its finest stretch, at Bedruthan Steps. I had no thought that a discovery made at just this spot would turn out to solve a critical wartime problem that for long had baffled many people.

Inksetter took great pleasure, until his stomach turned a bit acid, in the genuine rough cider that was easily available at country pubs in those days. The weather was excellent and the days soon slipped by, until it was time for us to foregather with the others at the Boswinger youth hostel near Gorran Haven. My memories are of days spent swimming and sunbathing on the local beach, and of several of us following the agile Bill Sessions on low, water-line traverses of mile after mile of rocky coastline. The youth hostel had a notable peculiarity. Each morning the farmer's wife would ask us whether we wanted ham or beef for supper. Day after day we said beef, and day after day it turned out to be ham. It was like Henry Ford I's remark: 'You can have it any colour you like, so long as it's black.'

It was while we were at Boswinger youth hostel that the results for the Mathematical Tripos were published. George Carson sent me a telegram. I had what was known as 'honours with distinction', which meant that I had attained my objective of being in the top ten. What I hadn't quite expected was to receive the Mayhew Prize, given for the best performance on the 'applied' mathematics side, which is to say in theoretical physics. More precisely, I had a half-share of the prize, the other half going to Stanley Rushbrooke, later Professor of Theoretical Physics at Newcastle. Only a year or two back I was out walking the hills on a winter day with Stanley. In later years we have often laughed at how we damned each other in the summer of 1936, for the prize was worth £25, and losing a half of it to somebody else was no light matter. The examination marks were not published in detail, but the share of the prize had to mean that I had managed to lift myself into the first three or four places on the list.

Not all members of the party at Boswinger were in their third year, needing to return to Cambridge for the Degree Day ceremony. The time came for those of us who were so involved to leave. Ivan Inksetter and I once more paired up for the trip. Although returning to a mini personal triumph in Cambridge, I left Cornwall for the heavily populated eastern region of England with regret, an indication that big city life was not for me. The return journey was an anti-climax after the exuberance of our outward journey three weeks before. My one vivid memory is of a very long ride that ended at a transport café near Stamford where we got a bed for the night. The ride was memorable for the tremendous thunderstorm through which we passed, and for a windscreen wiper that ceased to function.

The following morning was brilliantly fine, and we were in Cambridge by 9.00 a.m. Inksetter made his way to St John's and I to Emmanuel. In the following years I had a number of letters from Ivan, but I never saw him again in person after we parted that morning. In retrospect, I realise we have a built-in wrong attitude to human relationships. While they exist, we think they are for ever. If one travels abroad with friends or with one's family, the tendency is to take pictures of unusual inanimate objects – ancient temples or fine mountain scenes. The feeling is that the people around us are eternal and can be ignored, whereas a record must be made of the remarkable inanimate things we see in our lives. But just the opposite is true. The ancient temples are likely to be around for centuries to come, and the mountains for millions of years. It is the people who will soon be gone.

I had a day to spare before Degree Day on the morrow. I checked with Rudolf Peierls that he would accept me as a research student, and I checked with P. W. Wood that a letter would be sent on my behalf to the West Riding of Yorkshire. P.W. told me the Master of the College wanted to see me urgently. It was to swear me in officially as a Scholar. After my first year I had become an Exhibitioner, the old exhibition standard that I had sought to achieve from school. And now, with just one day to spare before graduating, I had at last achieved the scholarship standard. It seemed a long time since my oral interview with Ron Norrish on the occasion of that ill-fated attempt at the chemistry scholarship.

It was even a long way back to the day in October 1933 when I had arrived in Cambridge a frail young fellow weighing about 115 pounds, knowing little except the few things I had managed mostly to teach myself over the years. As I prepared for the Degree Day ceremony on the following day I stripped off and bathed. I was now about 150 pounds, quite hard physically after all the walking of the past years and the canoeing of the preceding weeks, and strongly browned by many days just spent in the Cornish sun. I had started on the Mathematical Tripos somewhere near the bottom of the slow stream and I had ended my undergraduate career somewhere near the top of the fast stream, almost infinitely higher than I had ever dared to hope.

With this said, I should admit there have been times when I have looked back to my school and university years with the niggling regret that until possibly my very last undergraduate term I never displayed anything of the competence of the golden child. My regret was partially allayed one morning in 1944. There were about a dozen of us in an office within a large, rambling school building which then housed the radar department of the British Admiralty. The purpose of our meeting was a review of the work of all the hundred or so persons employed in producing radar equipment for the Royal Navy. The review was made with a view to recommending upgradings and promotions in categories where they were deemed to have been well earned. There was one particular chap in his early twenties who had shown considerable experimental skill, who I thought should be promoted to a category normally reserved by the Civil Service for university graduates, which the young chap wasn't, at any rate at that time. I couldn't see why, with a war on and with the lad's work in my opinion of an appropriate standard, he shouldn't receive the promotion. The only other person who supported this view was Maurice Pryce. After the meeting as we walked together along a corridor, Maurice said to me with his wry smile: 'You know, Fred, the only two people who thought a degree wasn't important were the two with the best degrees.' My heart gave a bit of kick for I thought to myself: if Pryce thinks my degree good, it surely has to be.

In later life, Pryce and I got around one day to admitting that we had both envied the other. Why I had envied him was obvious. Why he envied me was that I had somehow managed to reach much the same position as himself seemingly out of nowhere. He told me of the psychological problems the golden child has to contend with. Once such a child becomes known outside family and school circles, the pressure never to slip becomes unremitting. If the widening circle of people who watch the golden child were truly sympathetic, the situation would be fine, like a home football team urged on by its supporters. But there are too many actively hoping for a slip, hoping they will be able to say to themselves: 'Ha ha! He's no better than I am.'

Ray Lyttleton, who will appear in my last chapter, once told me that in the year Bobby Jones won all the major golf championships Jones found himself obliged to hire bodyguards to prevent people from invading the course, ostensibly to advise him on how he should play his shots. I myself remember a letter in the national press from a reader who wished to inform the world that, while he would travel a hundred miles to watch Don Bradman field, he wouldn't walk ten yards to watch the man bat. The world is well stocked with people like that who feel compelled to degrade excellence of any kind in all manner of subtle and unsubtle ways. Tommy Gold refers to such people as those who 'seek to make a mark on history by making a mark on those who have made a mark on history'. The more I have seen of the world, the more I have come to think I was very lucky to have been permitted to develop in my own way, setting my own objectives instead of having them decided for me by the roar of the crowd.

Chapter Nine

I MENTIONED IN the previous chapter how in June 1936 I returned from a holiday in Cornwall to Cambridge with a sense of anti-climax. My emotion was real – I know that for sure. The reason I gave, a preference for rural rather than urban areas, seems the most innocent explanation, since to say anything different would be to claim a measure of prescience that appears unlikely. Science in Cambridge in the summer of 1936 was like a stock market riding high before a crash. By 1938–9 there were more visible causes for disquiet, but it seems rather far-fetched to suppose I could have seen anything untoward in 1936, at the very threshold of my research career.

Let me take the biggest matter first. From 1926 to 1936 physics had enjoyed a golden age. By 1938–9, however, Paul Dirac was to say: 'In 1926, people who were not very good could do important work. Today people who are very good cannot find important problems to solve.' This was the first clear warning I had that the euphoria which was still widespread in the summer of 1936 was misplaced.

Everybody had the idea that the triumphs of the

previous decade in atomic physics were going to be repeated in nuclear physics, an illusion which continued to bedevil science worldwide for another three decades. People found it easy to be deluded because of the apparently great success of empirical nuclear physics in the forties and fifties. An empirical approach to a subject is simply a look-see method. Suppose you want to know if salt dissolves in water. An obvious way to decide would be to try it and see. This would be the empirical approach. But if you understood in sufficient depth the basic nature of the atoms which constitute the molecules of salt and water you could settle the matter by calculation, without bothering with look-see at all. This would be what scientists call a fundamental approach. The success of nuclear physics in producing energy from reactors, and in producing devastating weapons – if you call that a success – came from the look-see method. To many, these successes appeared so striking that the illusion persisted.

The example of salt dissolving in water suggests wrongly that an empirical approach is simpler than a fundamental one. At the outset it is, but as time goes on the empirical approach becomes more and more complex, with epicycles piling on epicycles. The fundamental approach, on the other hand – when at last it succeeds – resolves into an amazing simplicity. The route towards the fundamental resolution of the nuclear problem has not turned out to lie in studying atomic nuclei at all, as scores of laboratories and hundreds of physicists through the forties and fifties believed would be the case. The route began in the study of cosmic rays, and then from the fifties onwards in the building of particle accelerators. From experiments with accelerators it became clear that the particles which make up atomic nuclei, protons and neutrons, are themselves composite. The components came to be called quarks, and from the mid-sixties theories of the properties of quarks were developed.

Many forms of theory appear at first sight to be possible, although in the end one particular theory will almost surely come to seem 'deeper' and more elegant than the others, with a future generation thinking the outcome should have been obvious just as we tend to think the outcome of struggles in physics in the past should have been obvious. Physicists in the eighties have come to feel this eventual outcome is now within sight, and from their work a fundamental understanding of atomic nuclei is at last emerging, half a century later than we thought in 1936.

The coping stone of the golden age was not yet in place in 1936, the coping stone known as quantum electrodynamics. We all thought this eventual achievement to be just around the corner. It seemed to be something that might appear in the physics journals at any moment. The lectures I'd attended by Rudolf Peierls in May 1936 gave an up-to-the-moment discussion of where quantum electrodynamics then stood, while the course by Max Born gave his own attempted solution of the ultimate problem. In effect, there seemed to all of us to be a big nugget of gold lying around somewhere, if only we could find it. This too was an illusion, but not as distant an illusion as the nuclear problem. Quantum electrodynamics was to resist the assaults of the world's foremost physicists of the time – Dirac, Heisenberg, Bohr, Pauli. When it did eventually fall in around 1950, it would be to a post-war generation of theoretical physicists younger than myself.

A generation of theoretical physicists is much shorter than a social generation – ten or fifteen years at most. I do not think physicists today would deny that my generation was the unluckiest of the past half century. We were too late to receive anything but crumbs from the rich table of the years around 1926, we were too early for quantum electrodynamics, and very much too early for quarks. Additionally from 1939 to 1945 we lost six wartime years, half the life of our generation. A perception of the way things were likely to go came gradually to me over the period 1937 to 1939, mainly I think because of my decision in 1937 to stand on my own feet, a decision I shall refer to in more detail in the next chapter. Others of my generation who continued regardless, sometimes because they were under the close direction of a 'supervisor' or research director, were, I think, less fortunate in not making a change of direction soon enough, or not making it at all.

At the time I returned to Cambridge from Cornwall in June 1936, the Cavendish Laboratory was one of the most famous, perhaps *the* most famous, centre of experimental physics in the world. There was nothing to tell us that the great Rutherford would die in 1937 or that, so far as fundamental physics was concerned, the Cavendish would soon opt out thereafter. It was to be like a highly prosperous company going into sudden liquidation. All of Rutherford's associates of any appreciable seniority were to leave, to be replaced from outside Cambridge by physicists who were not concerned with the more fundamental aspects of their subject. For form's sake, it has often been claimed that the exodus took place because the individuals in question saw opportunities elsewhere. But a group of men, mostly already well known to the world, would not lightly abandon *the* most famous laboratory. The exodus occurred co-operatively because Rutherford's associates were dismayed at decisions taken over the direction of the laboratory.

The demise of fundamental experimental physics in Cambridge inevitably had repercussions in theoretical physics. After the 1939–45 war, Cambridge was to produce a number of outstanding theoretical physicists, but every one of them left, never to return. A major reason for this second exodus was a gross efflorescence in the Faculty of Mathematics of a subject known as 'fluid mechanics' or 'continuum mechanics'. This subject had been given impetus by the need during the 1939–45 war for an understanding of aeronautics, and it continued growing thereafter due to the illusion that Britain would become a major exporter of commercial and military aircraft. It was a case of Gresham's Law, the bad driving out the good; or as a sixteenth-century writer remarked in respect of the spreading of ground-elder: 'It is so fruitful in its increase, that where it has once taken root, it will hardly be gotten out again, spoiling and getting every yeere more ground, to the annoyance of better herbes.'

Although in 1936 all this was but a distant cloud on the horizon, other darker clouds were nearing the zenith. The re-militarisation of the Rhineland by Hitler in March 1936 came as a dividing line for many people, myself included, between feeling incredulously that 'Surely war can't happen again,' to feeling that inexorably 'It *is* indeed going to happen again.' From 1936 to 1939 we oscillated between a despairing hope that war might be avoided and the equally despairing conviction that the sooner it came the better. To many people, again including myself, it seemed that the reoccupation of the Rhineland provided Britain and France with a last opportunity of cutting the Nazis down to size without involving the world in full-scale war. Disgust at the weakness of the British government was felt in many quarters. Ray Bell, later a Treasury mandarin and Vice-President of the European Investment Bank, was a member of the rambling club I described in the previous chapter. His parents lived in Bradford, and during April 1936 he and I did a longish walk in the environs of Ilkley, just before returning to Cambridge for my last undergraduate term. I was invited to dinner that night at the Bell household and I still remember the father saying with intense regret, but prophetically: 'If only Winston Churchill were Prime Minister now.'

Philip Dee, the same Dee who in early 1933 had given me a hard time in the Pembroke scholarship examination, was the most belligerent of the senior Cavendish staff. It must have been a year or so after the Rhineland fiasco that Dee said at tea-time in the Cavendish, 'I think it's time for a crack at them,' and I remember thinking to myself, 'He really means it!' When the war actually came Dee was the head of a group which produced a novel form of airborne radar, not for detecting a moving target like a plane, ship, or submarine, but for obtaining a detailed picture of the ground. It was the father of the kind of radar used in modern times for determining the surface topography of Venus.

In the previous chapter I described my personal responses to the pressures of undergraduate life. At this point, with wider issues now raised, I should perhaps say something of student life in general. The three periods 1930–33, 1933–6 and 1936–9 were, I think, pretty distinct. Those who passed their undergraduate years in the 1930–33 period were dominated in their thinking by the social misery of the depression years. This was the period that produced intellectual socialists of such great conviction that they maintained their views unswervingly for a lifetime. By 1933–6 the worst of the depression had passed, however. There was economic expansion with improving conditions and with lower unemployment. Interest in socialist economics waned. I remember being fiercely concerned with such matters in my later years at school (which is to say during the depression years themselves), but by 1933–6 the efforts of undergraduate representatives of the main political parties to canvass my interest were always met with a polite but firm no. The situation in Germany had begun to appear more relevant, but not yet grossly threatening. Consequently my own period, 1933–6, was one of exuberance, of economic improvement, of expansion – a cause for rejoicing generally.

Students today can hardly imagine what a difference the trappings of Empire made. For one thing, we had a wide spread of incoming students from all over the earth. For another, there were opportunities in the Foreign Service for any competent student who wished to move out into a world much larger than Britain itself. The face of Cambridge itself was subtly different from today, but since all this is excellently documented by easily obtained photographic collections it would be rather pointless to launch into descriptions of the old Corn Exchange, the old Guildhall, or the old Festival Theatre on Newmarket Road which we patronised before the advent of the Arts Theatre. Rather, let me dwell a moment on other issues – clothes for one. Ours was a woolly, baggy generation – huge baggy trousers, baggy caps, baggy jackets, with lots of air pockets and wool in them because of the cold buildings. We did not attend lectures in centrally-heated university buildings but in large, unheated rooms within colleges, which have now been subdivided and have consequently disappeared as lecture rooms. Almost every college had one such lecture room used by the general university population, and some colleges had several.

The tight-fitting clothes made of artificial fibres which are such a visually evident feature of undergraduate life today were impossible for us. Instead of simply mooching from one lecture room to another in the same university building as at present, at the end of each lecture we were thrown in all weathers literally into the street. Lectures were supposed to start five minutes after the hour and to end five minutes before the hour. We used the intervening ten minutes to walk, run or cycle from one college to another – the longest stretch for me being from St John's to Peterhouse. Because lecturers often infringed the five-minute rule, our ten-minute intervals could be much reduced, so that I would frequently be obliged either to run, or cadge a lift on somebody's bike step. A step was a solid steel extension to the axle of the rear wheel about three inches long on which you stood behind the rider. The trick was for the rider to get started slowly, and for you to run behind and lift your foot up onto the metal projection more or less in mid-stride, steadying yourself by putting a hand on the rider's shoulder. Under favourable conditions it wasn't a hard manoeuvre, but in wet weather in a crowded Cambridge street it needed a bit of practice. There were few motor vehicles in those days apart from the buses, which were about as frequent as they are now. So the streets were dominated by bicycles, particularly on the hour as undergraduates sped from lecture to lecture. Nobody took off their gown as they rode through the streets, not even if they were standing on somebody else's bike step.

Most undergraduates lived in so-called 'licensed lodgings', which were 'digs' in which your landlady or landlord kept a book on you. It was essential to be indoors and locked up for the night before 12.00 p.m., and if you did not get in before 10.00 p.m. a note was made of what was considered a slight misdemeanour. The same system continued for a while after the 1939–45 war. There was a Girton girl who ran up a fearsome total of late nights. Since she was not only very good-looking, but was also placed exceptionally high in the Mathematical Tripos, her case provoked another of Tommy Gold's classic remarks: 'All human abilities are positively correlated.'

The normal arrangement was for a male undergraduate to spend his first two undergraduate years in digs and the third year in college. Because my examination result in 1934 had been considered reasonably good, I profited by being assigned rooms in college already in my second year, thereby saving me quite a bit of bother. The digs in my first year near the railway bridge in Mill Road had involved me in a morning rush to reach a 9.00 a.m. lecture, and often enough an evening rush to avoid a late night. Too high a score of late nights could lead to being hauled in front of your tutor, although such things never amounted to much for students whose examination results were strong, as with the noteworthy girl from Girton. Added to other misdemeanours, however, too many late nights could lead to the phenomenon of 'rustication', and even in extreme cases of being 'sent down'. Being sent down amounted to your being summarily booted out, while being rusticated meant being temporarily dismissed from the university for some assigned period – usually the balance of a term, but in more extreme cases the balance of a year. The most famous misdemeanour in my time at Cambridge was perpetrated by a St John's undergraduate, the future England cricket captain Freddie Brown. At a special football dinner he took it into his head to jump up onto one of the long wooden tables and then dribble everything in sight on the table tops into the laps of fellow undergraduates sitting on either side of the table.

The university and college punishments were rudimentary survivals of a system that had been considerably more severe in earlier centuries, before the coming into existence of the police. The rules had been designed to prevent clashes between students and the indigenous population of Cambridge. They permitted tutors to keep students constantly in sight, to make sure, I suppose, that a tutor could efficiently inform parents whenever one of his charges had his throat cut by the locals. While you were in the system you were said to be *in statu pupillari*. You didn't get out of being *in statu pupillari* simply by graduating, as I had done in June 1936 when I had received the degree of Bachelor of Arts. To escape from being *in statu pupillari* you had to receive the Master of Arts degree, for which no examination performance is or was required. To become a Master of Arts you simply had to wait a further three years, in my case until June 1939.

To my blunt Yorkshire mind the system appeared

little short of ludicrous, although I accepted it and steered my way around it without difficulty – except on one occasion. This happened late in my years as a research student, just before I was due to receive elevation to Master of Arts. In a rush to attend an evening lecture I walked unwittingly onto the streets without my academic gown, and was hauled before a Junior Proctor for the oversight. Since the man was not much older than I was, and quite likely by that time did not have as good an academic record, I was quite annoyed about the incident. Yet I was never much of a sea lawyer. So after swallowing hard once or twice I accepted the situation, looking forward to the day, not so far off now, when I too would be *ex statu pupillari*.

The Cambridge disciplinary system even survived the post-war intake of students who had served with distinction in the armed forces, although it was severely tested one Guy Fawkes night by ex-army sappers who set off real high explosives in Senate House Passage. What eventually did it in, or greatly attenuated it, was all-powerful economics. Licensed digs were expensive in my time and eventually in post-war years they became prohibitively so, forcing colleges to provide internal accommodation, thereby effectively tripling the number of students housed on the spot. Inevitably, colleges have a generally more populated look today than they had in the thirties. During the mornings you then had crocodiles of students making their several ways into and out of colleges as they attended lectures in college classrooms, but in the afternoons things were much quieter. The dispersed state of the student body in the old licensed lodging system made coming together at night for dinner in college halls more important than it is now. We were obliged to pay for five such dinners a week – and having paid for them we ate them, of course.

A comparison of college halls today with the way they used to be provides much evidence against this monopoly. Emmanuel hall in 1933–6 was dark and forbidding for us captives: the food was not good and it was thrown at you with lightning speed, so that you simply gobbled the stuff and were out of the place long before the dons on High Table were half-way through their meal. Today, the same hall is pleasantly decorated, students do not walk about freely on the tops of tables as we did, they eat in a leisurely fashion, taking about as long over it as the dons. Moreover, a fair number of women are to be seen among them, so that you are not obliged to look down from the High Table on yet another of those Cambridge all-male dinners.

Dividing the thirties as I did before – 1930–33, 1933–6 and 1936–9 – my undergraduate years of 1933–6 were the lucky ones. We were not overshadowed by the gloom of the depression years; nor were we exposed to the overwhelming threat of war which became more and more repressive of spontaneity and ebullience as the thirties advanced. Yet even as early as June 1934 we were feeling some threat. I know this, because I still remember the flicker of hope with which I read garish headlines in the press on the weekend of 30 June in that year. This was the weekend when Ernst Röhm, the leader of the Nazi storm troopers, and his lieutenants were executed without trial. This was the 'Night of the Long Knives', as the newspapers called it. The thought was that thieves had turned at last against themselves. Over previous years Röhm had figured largely in the public eye, with details of the brutal behaviour of his stormtroopers extensively reported in the British press. But instead of breaking up summarily as we had hoped, the power of the Nazi party continued its mushroom-like growth unchecked, with the reoccupation of the Rhineland in 1936, the annexation of Austria in March 1938, and the invasion of Czechoslovakia in March 1939. If these issues had been hard-fought, as the contemporary battle at cricket between

Don Bradman and the English fast bowler Harold Larwood was hard-fought, that would have been acceptable. What did it in for us students was the intense feeling that we had of being sold down the river by our political leaders. We felt that the Nazi regime could have been suppressed early on with not much more than unpleasantness. If our political leaders felt legal justification to be necessary, it was amply provided by the reoccupation of the Rhineland.

By 1938–9 we felt that through total ineptness a game that might easily have been won had been converted into a game we were likely to lose; it was as if the defenders in a football match were to stand immobile, permitting the other side to score goals at will. The height of student disgust was reached during the Spanish Civil War (1936–9), a war that began as a military revolt against a legally-elected republican government which should, we students felt, have received whatever international support was going because of its legality. Instead, Italy and Germany were permitted to send overt aid to the rebels, while the British government refused to provide escorts for ships carrying supplies to the republicans, and even at one point impeded a ship's captain who tried to carry supplies unescorted – or at any rate so it was reported in the press. Anthony Eden was Foreign Secretary at the time. Eden resigned in February 1938, according to his biography in the *Encyclopaedia Britannica* to 'protest at Prime Minister Neville Chamberlain's appeasement of Nazi Germany and Fascist Italy'. But according to my information, Eden actually resigned because of more personal differences with the Prime Minister. Since my informant is a modern historian of high reputation, I would suppose his view of the matter is likely to be correct. If it is, we have an example here of how Neville Chamberlain has been cast as the goat for all the disastrous politics of the times. I will say a little more about Chamberlain in a moment.

It was in these circumstances that the Oxford Union passed in 1939 its since-famous motion, that the student members would not fight for King and Country. Much has been written, erroneously I believe, about this motion by later commentators who evidently do not understand the state of mind of those who supported it. Without actually experiencing the intense frustrations of the times it is even hard to understand what the students really meant by their vote. The vote was not pacifist in the usual sense. The students really meant that the inept politicians who had wantonly landed themselves in an unnecessary mess had better contrive to get themselves out of it without calling on the blood of a younger generation to make good their own mistakes and deficiencies. When war eventually came this well-justified point of view was still hard to slough off, and indeed there was a long, inactive introduction to the war, referred to in the press as the 'phoney war', while psychological adjustments were being made.

The reference to the King in the Oxford motion was perhaps understandable in view of the problems experienced by the monarchy in the thirties. The turn-around in popular esteem for the Royal Family came later, with the war itself, when George VI and the present Queen Mother refused to be budged out of London during the German blitzes.

Emmanuel College holds a commemoration feast annually in the first few days of December, and because of my now improved status in the college I was invited in December 1936. It was the first formal dinner I had attended. Luckily I had acquired evening dress for a function connected with the BA degree ceremony the previous June, so together with a newly-purchased BA gown I was more resplendent than I'd ever been heretofore. I was placed close to the don's table, towards the left-hand end facing up the hall, and so was in a good position to observe the High Table when the time came for the Royal Toast. Deciding this was an occasion to disregard old Mr Bartle's advice never to let a drop of alcohol pass my lips, I duly drank the Toast, my memory of Mr Bartle being suddenly erased by cries around me of 'The King, long may he reign, God bless him.' One old boy appeared to be in tears.

Three days later the news of the abdication of Edward was all over the newspapers. I was dumbfounded at the swiftness with which the notabilities seemed to have switched from their erstwhile cries of loyalty during the Toast to outright condemnation. If the truth be told, I was suddenly now more on Edward's side than I'd been at the feast. If these are the sort of friends one acquires higher up the social ladder then I don't want them, I thought to myself.

But the most distraught man in Cambridge was, remarkably enough, a Turk. His name was Ali Irfan. He had an enormous chest on him and had astonished the University Athletics Club on his first visit there by putting the heavy shot further than anyone in Britain had ever putted it before. In short, he looked a professional Turkish strong man, the kind who under Mustafa Kemal had hauled the guns which prevented our men from scaling the heights at Gallipoli in 1915. Together with a number of other young Turks, he had been sent as a student to Cambridge by the government in Istanbul, and as young people from alien cultures sometimes do he had absorbed himself deeply over the past two or three years into our own culture. On his return to Turkey Ali Irfan was to become a professor of English – at Ankara, I think. But now he was wrapped in gloom, declaring the situation to be among the most tragic in history. When George Carson and I visited him with the charitable aim of cheering him up, it was to find Ali Irfan playing ceaselessly on the gramophone the gloomiest of his considerable stock of Sibelius recordings.

In retrospect, the only politician in the British

governments of the thirties about whom I have second thoughts is Neville Chamberlain. He became Prime Minister in May 1937, which is to say after the main mistakes of British foreign policy had already been made. To the extent that Chamberlain had been Chancellor of the Exchequer under Baldwin, he carried some responsibility for the previous mistakes. But I would suppose that, while a Chancellor of the Exchequer can make his views on foreign policy known, he cannot regard foreign policy as his primary concern, otherwise he would soon be at loggerheads with the Foreign Secretary. While the Chamberlain government of 1937–9 outwardly pursued an appeasement policy, Britain underneath was actively preparing for war. The fighter planes and the radar screen which saved Britain in 1940 did not come out of nowhere. They were planned, designed and manufactured by the Chamberlain and earlier governments. Britain won the air battles of 1940 because the dates at which designs were frozen turned out to be optimally chosen. German designs were frozen earlier and their products were therefore not so technically good – in the air at any rate. All this eventually accrued to the advantage of Churchill's government, which in my opinion did not have the same positive technical flair as was shown in the Chamberlain era. Churchill did things politically right but often technically wrong, whereas Chamberlain did things technically right but politically wrong.

I have always been hoping for a well-informed reassessment of Chamberlain, but I suppose would-be biographers find it impossible to push against the millstone Chamberlain hung around his own neck when he flew back from Munich at the end of September 1938. Arriving in London he waved a paper at the waiting crowd, saying, 'It's peace in our time.' Against such a clanger, given enormous coverage in the newspapers of course, even biographers must fight in vain.

I have often wondered why the 1939–45 war broke out when it did. The explanation usually offered, namely that in early September 1939 Germany invaded Poland, is a truism, not an explanation. Germany had already invaded Austria and Czechoslovakia, both in bad faith, without war breaking out. The answer, I believe, lies in the club atmosphere that leaders of nations generate for themselves, an atmosphere which nowadays obviously manifests itself in their widely advertised summit meetings. The qualification for club membership is, and was, that a leader be legally elected by his or her country. In this respect, Hitler took great care to be elected to the German Chancellorship through properly constituted elections. Once elected, a club member is immediately accorded a considerable measure of trust and goodwill, a measure so great that Hitler did not dissipate it entirely in the eyes of western political leaders until 1938–9. The reason why we students took such a very different view was that we considered that all trust and goodwill should have been dissipated already when the German police state was set up as early as 1934. The fact that we were proved correct should be no surprise for, to reveal a deep truth, young people do most everything better than old people.

I come now to a question I have been asked many times. Was there anything I saw over the years 1933–9 to suggest that Cambridge was harbouring a nest of traitors owing allegiance to the Soviet Union? The answer is a plain no. There was, of course, plenty of evidence of Soviet propaganda. There was the *Daily Worker* on sale every weekday, with yards of Soviet propaganda plastered all over it. The biologist J.B.S. Haldane wrote science articles for the *Daily Worker* – little gems which many of us enjoyed reading. Haldane was a convinced Marxist who gave lectures to university audiences up and down the country. In 1938 I attended one myself, and I can say with total conviction that no prospective traitor could ever have been won over by such stuff. Haldane's lecture was so full of Marxist jargon as to be incomprehensible, unless you were a confirmed Marxist already. I was amazed that a man who could write such beautiful science articles could talk such codswallop. Like George Orwell, Haldane eventually turned away from Marxism, and for the same reason – the Soviet police state. In the fifties I had a long correspondence with Haldane in the course of which he remarked: 'Every one of my friends among Russian biologists has been removed from his post, and some have disappeared.' This caused Haldane to resign his foreign membership of the Academy of Sciences of the USSR. As he said himself, it was his second conversion, something which any sensible person who has anything to do with the Soviet Union is likely to experience eventually.

Soviet propaganda made great play with the fact that the strongest opposition to Hitler in the pre-1933 period had come from the German communist party. Soviet propaganda also claimed, I suspect with more cunning than reality, to be sending arms to the legally elected republicans in Spain. Since the first of these protestations was true, we were mostly tricked into believing the second was true. So it came about that the Soviet Union acquired goodwill from next to nothing it had actually done itself. For a while indeed, especially in 1938, the Soviet Union was able to represent itself as the only source of determined opposition to the rise of Hitler. But in August 1939 Stalin concluded a non-aggression pact with Hitler, which showed all the previous claims to have been a sham. British communists did what they could to save something from the wreckage by strenuously maintaining that the Soviet Union had been forced to this drastic step through the refusals of Western governments, the British government particularly, to take effective steps to limit German aggression. That this was a flat communist lie, of the kind which turned George Orwell around in Spain, was plain for all but a nincompoop to see when on 3 September, only a week or two after the Stalin–Hitler pact, Britain declared war on Germany.

In retrospect, the wild lurchings of the communist newspaper the *Daily Worker*, particularly over the month preceding the outbreak of war, made hilarious reading. Here are a few headlines:

3 August: FEARS OF NEW BETRAYAL BY PREMIER
7 August: STEP TO SURRENDER DANZIG
13 August: DRAMATIC MOVE TO STOP PREMIER'S SURRENDER

To this point, Chamberlain was a peacemonger condemned for refusing to join the Soviet Union in its resolute stand against fascist tyranny. Then, most unfortunately for the *Worker*, came the Soviet–German non-aggression pact, which really opened the route to war. The *Worker* instantly went into reverse with a visible stripping of its gears:

23 August: SOVIET'S DRAMATIC PEACE MOVE A THUNDERBOLT FOR THE CHAMBERLAIN CABINET
26 August: RUSSIA SHATTERS AXIS
28 August: CHAMBERLAIN, WRECKER OF PEACE MOVES

So in only a couple of weeks the wretched Chamberlain was transmogrified by flagrant witchcraft from peacemonger to warmonger. And on 1 September the *Worker* exceeded itself by shuffling a further miracle from its sleeve, a document 'which reveals the extent to which the German Government has been shaken by the Soviet–German Non-Aggression Pact'. What the *Worker* should properly have told its readers, of course, was that the so-called non-aggression pact was actually an aggression pact, whereby Russia and Germany had agreed to carve up Poland between them. So far from the German government being shaken, by 1 September the German war machine had moved to full speed ahead, with consequences that by 3 September had become very clear to all of us.

How, in these circumstances, any intelligent person could bring himself actively to spy for the Soviet Union remains hard to understand. Of course, anybody who in 1938 had become politically and economically convinced that the Soviet Union was destined to be the saviour of the world could be expected to make all sorts of excuses for Soviet behaviour in 1939–40. There were such people in fair numbers around Cambridge, but none of them looked then, or even now with the benefit of hindsight, remotely like a spy. Some quite different psychological component other than I encountered in my day-to-day experiences at Cambridge was needed to produce a spy.

There was a bald-headed communist Member of Parliament called Pritt, D.N. Pritt, who went around during the so-called phoney war of 1940 addressing audiences in universities. He published a book called *Must the War Spread?* Its purport was that the war had been started by Western capitalists in order to fuel their profits, for which reason an expansion of the early, inactive period of hostilities into full-scale war should be prevented. I attended one of Pritt's addresses and found difficulty at the time in understanding his motivation. Presumably there was already a fear in communist circles that, if the European conflagration really got under way, the Soviet Union would eventually become involved willy-nilly. So British policy, the firm policy we had all wanted to see adopted for so many years, was to be negated, according to Pritt, to suit the interests of the Soviet Union. In Britain such talk was permitted as fair comment, but if Pritt had been Russian and had gone around trying to subvert Soviet policy in the British interest he would surely have found himself on the wrong side of a firing squad. So even in wartime British tolerance was still broad, and it certainly took something quite out of the ordinary to produce a person who was overtly a spy by our permissive standards.

Rather the same, up to the summer of 1939, could be said for Bertrand Russell as for Pritt. In the spring of 1939 I attended a crowded evening talk given in Trinity College by Russell. He was a slender man with the thinker's classic forehead, thoughtful eyes, aquiline nose, and a firm mouth strengthened by being frequently clamped on the stem of his pipe. It was a face which, from the standpoint of my own pudding-basin features, I gazed at in envy. Russell's speech was incisive, his sentences well formed and completed – unlike Eddington who never in my experience finished a sentence even over a whole hour's lecture. If there was a flaw at all in Russell's manner of presentation, it was that his voice lacked the deeper timbres, but it was certainly not squeaky like H.G. Wells'.

Russell had perceived what later became known as the strategy of deterrence – the idea that each nation in a political stand-off possesses such terrifying weapons of destruction that both are obliged in the common interest to maintain the peace. This was fine as an intellectual concept, and in the later era of nuclear weapons it became apposite. What was not so fine was Russell's identification of the bomber forces of Germany and of the Western allies as weapons of terrifying deterrence. If war came with Germany, every major city on both sides would be totally destroyed, he told us, an opinion which turned out to be untrue. Being at the receiving end of a bombing raid was always highly unpleasant, but in Britain fortunately it was not the overwhelming disaster that would have been needed to give strategic substance to Russell's argument. Since I was to spend most of the war years close to the south coast of England I was to experience many bombing raids, fortunately without personal disaster. Statistically, too, the number of British lives lost in the Second World War was to be less than a fifth of the number lost in the 1914–18 war. So it remains a question how Russell came to make such a critical, morale-destroying mistake. I can hardly believe he was privy to the latest technological aspects of aeroplane design, nor does it seem likely that he was in receipt of special information from high-ranking officers of the Royal Air Force. Therefore he must simply have been guessing, and to what purpose? To urge on us a continuation of appeasement – what else? If Russell had toured German universities expressing the same point of view, that would have evened out the situation, but had he done so he would undoubtedly have been given very short shrift. There was the same lack of balance as in the case of D. N. Pritt, but with Germany profiting from the propaganda instead of the Soviet Union. With this said, let me emphasise that, whereas Russell immediately desisted once the war started, the communist propaganda continued unabated.

The big surprise eventually proved to be that the Soviet spies were not at all at the *Daily Worker* level, with connections to the official communist party, but in comparatively high society, in comfortable armchairs at the Foreign Office and elsewhere. How could this possibly have come about? Attendance at Bertrand Russell's talk in the spring of 1939 gave me my first glimpse of a new kind of person, one I hadn't encountered before, a person with the divine right of class. The divine right of class does not necessarily mean a person overtly throwing his or her weight around. In Russell's case it was quite the reverse. Russell did not throw the considerable weight of his class around, which was why he was widely and affectionately popular in academic circles. Typical of his popularity was a remark of Harold Jeffreys, the St John's mathematician, who said, apropos of certain of Russell's earlier somewhat lurid activities, 'What Bertie never understood is that in British society you can either advocate adultery or practise it, but not both.' The divine right of class implies the possession of an aura, an aura which gives others the feeling that in any matter of real urgency you can get things done behind the scenes in ways that are not open to discussion.

The divine right of class was the component in the Cambridge spy story that remained hidden from me during my student years. Nobody I knew had it. There were plenty of people I knew who were disaffected with the political situation, plenty who were in some degree deluded by Soviet propaganda, as I suppose I was myself. But without the divine right of class, without the notion you could manage to get things done subtly behind the scenes, the chaps I knew raged impotently.

There is no mystery about why the spies were concentrated in Trinity College, because the divine right of class was itself heavily concentrated there, with Russell and scores of others who were not spies. There was a type who wore jodhpurs and what then seemed very minute flat caps, and who shouted in remarkably penetrating voices at each other across Trinity Street, totally ignoring everybody else in the vicinity. This type would shortly be flying planes and driving tanks, for it was not disaffected or disgruntled. The disgruntled spy type did not shout across Trinity Street for the world to notice. He closeted himself indoors, plotting, out of sight of students like myself. Although we were disheartened by the political situation, we were not disgruntled because we felt, with just cause, that we were lucky to be there at all.

Chapter Ten

TURNING ONCE more to my personal affairs, while the step from undergraduate to BA status in 1936 did not permit me to escape from being *in statu pupillari*, it did bring a release from the discipline of late nights, so I could avoid the expense of living either in college or in licensed digs. The shift to unlicensed lodgings saved me about £50 a year, while the disappearance of college teaching fees saved another £20. Instead of the difference between £225 – the amount the West Riding education authorities continued to pay me – and my unavoidable expenses being only £25 as it had been before, my cash in hand soared in June 1936 to an annual amount approaching £100. That wasn't sufficient to compete with the lads in jodhpurs and small flat caps, but after the necessary frugality I'd developed over the years there seemed to be a touch of real wealth about it.

Until 1937 I shared digs with Charles Goodwin in Station Road; it was here that we had listened to Beethoven's Emperor Concerto on the evening of the forty-mile walk I described in an earlier chapter. I learned from Charles that the next thing to aim for was one of a number of research prizes awarded each year. Usually two first-level awards called Smith's Prizes were given, but there were also two or more Rayleigh Prizes, and gaining either a Smith's or Rayleigh was considered to be almost a guarantee of a post in some university. This, then, was the objective as I began my research career early in July 1936.

The time available was only four terms. A research essay had to be finished and submitted by December 1937, so it was essential to be away to a fast start. Partly because Rudolf Peierls was an enthusiastic research supervisor who fed me with two good up-to-date problems, and partly because I was already talking freely with research students during my last undergraduate year, I was able to hit the ground running, as Americans say. This was a considerable initial advantage, because most research students for whom Cambridge was their first and only university found the four terms too short. Why the university had decided that its regulations should be a handicap to its own graduates, who were greatly disadvantaged compared to research students coming from other universities, was a mystery. The slow undergraduate stream in which I had started was indeed entirely excluded by considerations of timing. Had I not made the risky jump in the summer of 1934 from the slow undergraduate stream in mathematics to the fast stream, I would never have been given a chance at these later research prizes, which were to prove pivotal for me. An important immediate advantage was that I could validly represent the prizes as the last performance test of my educational career, an argument which the Yorkshire West Riding authorities accepted with characteristic generosity by continuing my scholarship to the end of my second year of research, which is to say until the summer of 1938.

The day came when I handed in my shot at the prizes. The day also came towards the end of the Lent term in 1938 when the results were announced. As I had dared to hope, I had been awarded one of the two Smith's Prizes. As I had not expected at all, the two Smith's Prizes had unusually been placed in order of merit, a first and a second, and I had the first. It had been a long climb at Cambridge – three-quarters of the way up the slow stream in the first year, three-fifths up the fast stream in the second year, among the top three or four in the third year, and now, half-way through the fifth year, the top position itself.

It was twelve years almost to the day since I had walked, accompanied by the mumps virus, down from my home village to the cold schoolroom close by Holy Trinity Church in the poor eastern section of Bingley, when I had just squeaked by a hair's breadth through to my first scholarship award. I had been supported ever since by the West Riding of Yorkshire with its educational headquarters at Wakefield, a town centrally placed among the 'dark satanic mills' covering much of the region. Now, at the end of it all, I wrote to the Chairman of the Educational Committee in Wakefield with my thanks for the huge measure of support I had received, support which I doubt any other county in England would have given me.

This happy termination of my connection with the West Riding of Yorkshire meant I must look for a new source of support, rather like a floppy dog with a big tail a-wagging looking for a new master. My eye lit on the Goldsmiths' Company, a rich master if ever there was one. The Goldsmiths' Company offered a magnificent exhibition of £350 a year, but open to a wide range of candidates unfortunately. Applications had to be submitted by Easter with the names of two referees. Peierls agreed to be one and I had the idea of asking R. H. Fowler to be the other. This was a little unusual because I was not one of Fowler's own students, of which he had many. But I felt I had a small measure of credit with Fowler, for a reason I will now explain.

There was a room in the old Cavendish built by James Clerk Maxwell in about 1875 where a deal of blood was spilt in 1937 on a weekly basis. You went up two flights of stone steps to the first floor and then turned right up a further short flight of wooden steps, again turning right shortly thereafter into what was called the colloquium room, but which was actually a torture room – at any rate for those who gave theoretical physics colloquia in it in those days. Since no less a person than Eddington had spilt a vatful in that room, there was no reason why so minor a person as myself should escape the savage treatment handed out by the fearsome front row – Fowler, his buddy C. G. Darwin, A. H. Wilson, Dirac, and of course the sharp-witted Maurice Pryce, who was especially severe on poor Eddington. Eddington was never at his best in verbal battles and on the occasion in question he mistakenly tried to maintain that black was white, with truly awful results. The issue was the correct pressure formula for relativistically degenerate electrons. E. C. Stoner had used the formula physicists believed to be correct to show there was no permanent condition for a large enough quantity of matter, a quantity now known as the Chandrasekhar limit, except as a black hole. Eddington thought black holes should be a physical impossibility, so he inferred that the correct formula must be something else – actually the non-relativistic formula first used by R. H. Fowler himself.

In my very first term as a research student somebody had the idea of assigning to a chosen student each week a chapter from a big article on nuclear physics which had just then appeared in the *Reviews of Modern Physics*. Eight victims had to be found, mostly second and third year students like the three Maurices, Pryce, Goldhaber – later the director of the Brookhaven Laboratory on Long Island, New York – and Blackman. I believe I was the only first year student to be assigned a chapter, to come late in the term, Peierls assured me. This was a shocker of a situation, partly because the later chapters were pernickety details rather than interesting issues of principle, and partly because the big shots did their worst to bait Pryce who came early in the term, and this opening fracas set the tone for the no-holds-barred violence of succeeding weeks. When it came to my turn I was saved from being mangled to death only by the gong. Time ran out, permitting Peierls to suggest that my chapter, being a long one, should be finished the following week. He insisted I should spend the whole week of grace thus vouchsafed to me in further preparation, which I did, viewing the thing more as a research project than as a simple reporting of what somebody else had written. This helped, and in the event I escaped without too many more deep wounds. It was this escape out of the bear trap which had given me a little credit with Fowler. Now, as I tapped on the door of his office clutching an application form for the Goldsmiths' exhibition, was the time to use it.

There was a bark from inside the office which I took to mean 'Come in.' I went in and asked Fowler if he would act as a referee. He agreed immediately and gave a nod, as if to say, 'That's that, out you go.' So out I went, with my form duly completed. A few weeks later I had the Goldsmith's exhibition, worth £350 for the year 1938–9. Suddenly I was wealthy, fully able to buy jodhpurs and a small flat cap if I'd been of a mind to do so.

Getting into Fowler's office or rooms was no mean feat, actually. Pryce always told how, when Fowler was his undergraduate supervisor, he would go along each week to Fowler's rooms in Trinity. Fowler would respond to his knock by opening the door a few inches, just sufficient to admit a hand and arm. Out would come Fowler's hand clutching the exercises – examples we called them – which Pryce had handed in the previous week. Pryce would take them and push into Fowler's now empty hand his current week's work. The hand would then be withdrawn and a voice from the far side of the door would bark: 'Excellent, Pryce. Work more examples. Work more examples.' Then the door would shut firmly.

I have remarked before on how people enter our lives, how they fill the stage brightly for a while, and then fade away as in a dream. So it was now with many friends I had known in my undergraduate years. Each year I had gone to the mountains in the summer. In August 1936 a party from the rambling club, joined by Edward Foster, my companion of previous years, made a trip to harder mountains than I had seen before – the Cuillins of Skye. We toughed it out in a midge-ridden camp in Glenbrittle. Although we now were putting our lives literally in each other's hands since we were climbing on ropes, even so tight a bond was unable to withstand the swirling currents which dominate the river of life. After two years at school with Edward Foster and three summers of walking, I was never to walk the hills with him again, or indeed with any except one of that party of 1936. The exception was Joe Jennings who emigrated to Australia in the mid-1950s. Whenever I visited Australia thereafter I contrived to see Joe and to make a trip with him, and whenever he visited Britain we did the same. In August 1937 I was again in Glenbrittle, again with members of the rambling club, but the composition of the party had changed. They were a year junior to the previous year – or more accurately they were the same with respect to university status and I had grown a year older. And in August 1938 I was in Glenbrittle once more, alone. My undergraduate friends had vanished into the mists of life, just as surely as had the village lads with whom I had once spent so many vibrant hours. While mountains, buildings and organisations persist, friends will be gone pitifully soon, like mayflies on a summer day.

In 1937 Rudolf Peierls was also gone, to the Professorship of Applied Mathematics at Birmingham University.

I now had an important decision to make – to stay in Cambridge and go it alone, to stay in Cambridge with a new research supervisor and research topics, or to follow Peierls to Birmingham. Because I owed much to Peierls for the way he had pressed me quickly forwards the previous year, and because he seemed to want me to continue research with him, I felt I must give the possibility of a move to Birmingham first trial. But when I returned to Cambridge, ostensibly for just a weekend in mid-February, and found early crocuses bright and shining all along the avenue of Trinity Backs, I knew it couldn't be. I have two remaining memories of the several weeks I spent in Birmingham. One is of eating meals in a boarding house with other guests, breakfast and dinner together every day. It wasn't that I had anything against any one of them; it was just that we had no interests in common except cricket and the weather. As a substitute for nightly dinner at the Friar House with research students from the Cavendish it didn't fly, as people say. My other memory is of hearing Felix Weingartner conduct the Birmingham Symphony Orchestra, so establishing a bridge in time between Richard Wagner and my own day. People who nowadays appear to judge the quality of conductors from the extravagance of their gestures would have been amazed at the almost minute signals Weingartner gave to the orchestra. He remarks in his autobiography that anybody who conducted a different opera every night, as he had done as a young man in one of his first posts, would soon become economical of gesture. The programme opened with Schubert's *Rosamunde* overture, but the rest of it escapes me now.

The thought of switching to new research topics under a new supervisor didn't fly either. So it almost amounted to going it alone – but not quite, as it happened. A second problem Peierls had started me on went under the name of analysing the properties of wave equations of higher spin, higher spin than Dirac's famous equation. It amounted in modern terminology to determining the irreducible representations of products of the spinor group with itself. In those days, unfortunately, I knew no group theory, and consequently made a fist of the thing. The accidental feature was that Maurice Pryce also had an interest in the problem on his own account. So too had Wolfgang Pauli in Switzerland. There was a rumour that Pauli together with a student, Marcus Fierz, had obtained a certain result. I remember sitting in the Whim Café with Pryce and Peierls. They disagreed over whether the result was true or not, and Peierls said he'd bet a bob on it, but I can't remember which way round the bet went or who won it.

The supervisor problem, once I'd decided I wasn't leaving Cambridge, was simply that the university liked every research student to have a supervisor, although it wasn't absolutely essential unless you held a government grant from DSIR, or unless you wished to acquire a Ph.D degree. The Ph.D was not looked on as a crucial qualification in those days, but if I wanted to keep my options open on it I needed a supervisor. In view of Pryce's interest in the wave-equation problem, and Pryce having recently become a Fellow of Trinity, so removing him from being *in statu pupillari*, Peierls suggested to Pryce and to me that he should become my supervisor, which suggestion we both accepted.

The situation proved ironic, for if it had ever been my intention to seek the Ph.D, it was Pryce who persuaded me out of it. He had a dislike for the degree, which he regarded as a debasement of the academic currency. He showed his opinion by fulfilling all the technical requirements but then omitting ever to go to the Senate House to formalise the situation in an official ceremony. As it turned out I did the same, but only partly for doctrinaire reasons. I discovered the Inland Revenue distinguished between students and non-students by whether or not you had acquired the Ph.D, and since the distinction affected my tax quite substantially in the period 1939–41, I had a more earthy motive for avoiding an official ceremony in the Senate House. When Ray Lyttleton, who will enter my story in a moment, discovered what Pryce had done, he was annoyed that he hadn't thought to do the same himself, and for a while Lyttleton went around Cambridge saying he would sell his Ph.D for £10 – the cost of his Ph.D gown.

It would be a mistake to think this precious. It was an accurate perception of the damage to originality which slavish pursuit of this degree has caused. If a student wishes to study for the degree, particularly in cases where there is a change of university, well and good. But students in general who have gone from the age of five to the age of twenty-one through a never-ending sequence of examinations should by then be released from formal processing. It is high time at twenty-one to begin thinking for oneself. More and more as the years pass by, research students have come to accept close direction from supervisors, so consuming still another three or four years of the precious few in which the originality of childhood can reassert itself. The mere fact that government bureaucracy demands the Ph.D, and has demanded it pretty well from the first moment it was introduced from America, is sufficient to condemn it. The American educational system is different. It puts less pressure on the earlier years, better permitting originality to survive, and so giving the technical aspect of the Ph.D more of a *raison d'être* than it has in Britain.

I continued for a while on a problem I had begun with Peierls. It involved beta-decay occurring through intermediate states of the daughter nucleus. I am not sure if it was the first investigation of its kind, but it was new to senior physicists in the Cavendish Laboratory. They became interested, and as a consequence I was invited to attend their weekly meetings, just as Peierls had done until he left for Birmingham. Since Rutherford had died in 1937, the laboratory was being run in 1938 (before the arrival of Rutherford's successor) by John Cockroft, together with a consortium including Norman Fowler, Bennett Lewis (who was later to be the designer of the highly successful Canadian nuclear reactor CANDU) and Philip Dee. Seeing the laboratory was eventually to be shifted drastically in a direction away from nuclear physics, Chadwick, the discoverer of the neutron, had left already. My association with this senior group up to the summer of 1939 had a determining effect on my relations with Cambridge physics. I began in research by feeling that the Cavendish Laboratory was my home. When the big changes came, changes I described in the previous chapter, the Cavendish was no longer my home. Quite the reverse. I eventually became one of the few people left in Cambridge with emotional ties to the pre-war Cavendish. My feeling of eviction became the source of a tension that could never be resolved and which led eventually, far down the years, to my leaving Cambridge.

This was the opportunity for me to ask Philip Dee if he remembered the Yorkshire boy who had sparked back at him in the Pembroke scholarship examination, when he'd asked: 'Is there *any* physics you *do* know?' There was no way I could now dig the incident out of his memory. Dee brushed it aside with a wave of his arm: 'Oh, I say that sort of thing all the time,' he remarked airily. John Cockroft was the money man of the group. Whenever an experiment was proposed, Cockroft would set to work to figure out the cost. The conversation would linger on for a while, but as John came towards his final addition a dead silence would fall on the room. The usual thing was for Cockroft to give his friendly, half-sad smile, and shake his head, saying: 'Too much lead.' I should explain that lead was the standard material for shielding against nuclear radiations, and that its cost was often critical in relation to the minuscule sums then available, a far cry indeed from the unctuously rich later days at the Science and Engineering Research Council. The small committee was forever jumping on Bennett Lewis, demanding that he produce electronic equipment faster than he could produce it, and Philip Dee was forever exclaiming: 'Let's get on with it!'

The news was out that Erwin Schrödinger would be paying a visit to Cambridge, and I was allotted half an hour of his time at the Cavendish to explain beta-decay through intermediate states. I had barely begun to talk about the thing when I could see that Schrödinger wasn't really interested, and I had the flash of common sense to wonder why a man who had discovered the famous wave equation should be in the least interested in a question of whether nuclei decayed through intermediate states or not. My next meeting with Schrödinger would not be for some fourteen years, and it would then be in circumstances more different than you could imagine.

To take in this later occasion, my narrative must make a wide sweep. In around 1950, the Royal Astronomical Society held a meeting in Dublin, which my wife to be and I attended. At a pre-meeting gathering, I was introduced to Monsignor Browne, President of University College Galway. Paddy Browne, as he was known everywhere throughout Eire, had been gifted with talents that were almost too great for any one man to assimilate. He had begun with a Ph.D in mathematics from Göttingen, which meant that he spoke German fluently, just as he did French, Italian, Gaelic, Latin, ancient Greek – anything at all, in fact, which he happened to take a look at.

It was Paddy Browne who introduced me to the poetry of Erwin Schrödinger, which appears to be all but unknown to the scientific world. Schrödinger was then at the Dublin Institute of Advanced Studies, which fell under the University of Ireland, and so, since Paddy had become Chancellor of the University, the Institute was under Paddy's jurisdiction. One day in 1952 I was with him in Dublin when he said: 'We're going out this afternoon to tea with Schrödinger. I'm going to give him a dressing down.'

Getting a dressing down from Paddy, if he was in earnest, would have been a formidable business. He was a big man, about six feet four inches I suppose, with a big voice and a truly awesome command of words. In the car on the way to the Schrödinger home I asked what the trouble was. 'Oh,' said Paddy, 'there is to be a great reception by the President [of Eire]. We each have an invitation, for ourselves and a lady guest. Schrödinger wants me to take his wife, so that he can take Miss Y.'

Now I knew why Schrödinger hadn't been interested in beta-decay through intermediate states. 'Miss Y?' I asked. 'Ah,' continued Paddy, 'I must tell you that Miss Y is one of the beauties of all Ireland. Why else do you think Schrödinger would write poetry?'

Schrödinger was heartily glad to see me that day, for I was a kind of human tree behind which he could circle to dodge away from Paddy. He did this by talking about science, any old science, by handing round cups of tea and sandwiches, playing for time and, I suppose, for Miss Y. It has always been a matter of regret to me that I never saw a picture of Miss Y, but I still have a clear picture of Schrödinger dodging Paddy's assault with the agility of a matador in front of a bull.

Charles Goodwin had gone now, in 1938, to a post in the mathematics department at Sheffield University. So I moved from Station Road to the Chesterton region at the opposite side of the town, where I shared digs with George Carson. Gone now was our swiftest canoe on the river. George and I were still fairly fast, but it had been Charles' enthusiasm which had really kept us up to concert pitch. My extra-curricular conversations these days were mostly in biology, and it was through George that I met one of the outstanding biologists of the time,

C.D. Darlington. This meeting would exert a considerable influence on me down the years.

With Charles Goodwin gone, it was natural that I should take advantage of the circumstance that I was in a similar age relationship to Maurice Pryce, and that I could now drop in from time to time at his rooms in Trinity. Thirty years on from those days, Pryce was to tell me how much he regretted he hadn't published more. Pryce had a perfectionist attitude which made it hard for him to publish steps along the road in the manner of progress reports, the way most of us do. With Maurice it had to be a perfect and complete solution of a problem, usually a big one. In view of the fallow period into which physics was then running this attitude must have made life tough. Pryce would also circulate his manuscripts freely and generously, and in at least one case the work eventually appeared under other authorship. In around 1959 I received several significant and useful pages from Maurice, with an accompanying note saying he'd come on them in clearing out his files, and that 'possibly I might find the pages of interest'. He also added that he hadn't published the work, which dealt with certain mathematical aspects of the creation of matter in cosmology, because he'd not been successful in finding a connection to the then known theories of particle physics. The connection came eventually in the early 1980s, with the development of what are called 'grand unification theories'. This was typical of Maurice – always looking for connections that lay too far ahead in time.

He also had what seemed like a compulsive wanderlust – first Cambridge to Liverpool, then back to Cambridge, then to Oxford, to Bristol, to the University of Southern California, and finally to British Columbia, which curiously enough, he told me, even in those early years, he thought the most beautiful place on Earth.

I have only one thing to say against Pryce. Because of

his wanderlust it chanced from time to time in later years that I would be giving a lecture in a university where Maurice happened to be at the time. He would then take it on himself to introduce me to the audience with stories of how I had been a hellbroth of a research student, who had been wished onto him because nobody else at Cambridge could cope with me. This was pure calumny. I was always a model research student, and if any tricks were played at all, it was Maurice himself who played them, as the following small anecdote shows.

There was a research group with a limited membership which met in the evenings, once a fortnight I believe, called the Delta-Squared V Club. Whenever a place in the membership fell vacant, candidates to fill it would be proposed, and a vote by existing members would then decide the winner. During 1936–7 I had twice been proposed but had not made it on the vote. In 1938, Pryce, who was then the club's Secretary, again proposed me, and to my surprise I won in a near landslide that seemed to amuse several persons present at the meeting, which I had attended by invitation. The system in the club was that after serving a specific time, which I think was a term, the President stood down and the Secretary took his place. So it was with Pryce at this particular meeting. Once in the Presidential chair, Pryce immediately proposed me for the now-vacant post of Secretary, and I again won in a landslide, amid much laughter as it was realised how I'd been limed and snared into a job with a considerable amount of work to it – arranging the venue of meetings, which by tradition swung from college to college as the Secretary changed, writing up minutes, obtaining speakers and making abstracts of their talks, and generally standing up to the barrage of pointed comments with which meetings always began. On the way out after the meeting, Pryce grinned and said: 'Let that be a lesson not to trust anybody, not even your supervisor.'

The most awkward part of the Secretary's duties was to find speakers. Since Pryce had just been Secretary, I asked if he had any suggestions. 'You might try Dirac,' he replied, 'and there's a chap in John's called Lyttleton who has interesting ideas about planets.' The next day I took my courage in both hands and phoned Dirac at his house. When he had understood my request, Dirac made a remark which nobody else in my experience would have conceived of: 'I will put the telephone down for a minute and think, and then speak again,' he said.

The upshot was that Dirac agreed to give a talk to the club, and a famous talk it was, for it was the first occasion on which Dirac explained his idea for introducing advanced potentials to solve the paradox of the self-action of a classically accelerated electron. My attempt to get Ray Lyttleton to give a talk to the Delta-Squared V Club was not so successful. I visited him in his rooms in the New Court of St John's at about three o'clock one afternoon. In reply to my request he explained that he was snowed under with work from which he could in no circumstances be dragged. In 1945–6 I was to have those same rooms myself, above the Bursary (as it was then) on Staircase I. Withdrawing from my failure to entice Lyttleton into appearing before the Delta-Squared V Club, I was crossing the yard or two of a small hallway when a thought occurred to me. Almost certainly my life would have gone differently in its details if, in that fleeting second, the thought had not been there. I turned impulsively on my heel, moved the yard or two back to the inner door, half-opened it without knocking, stuck my head inside and said: 'I hope I can do as much for you another time.'

I hadn't realised it, but my remark was exactly the sort of thing that sets Ray Lyttleton off laughing. He called me back immediately and put on the kettle for tea. He was friendly now, but try as I would I couldn't persuade him to give that lecture to the Delta-Squared V Club. He talked of being on the verge of great things, of vast depths, in the fashion of Owen Glendower in *Henry IV, Part I*.

The immediate problem for Lyttleton had to do with the rate at which the gravitational influence of a large body causes it to pick up material from a diffuse gas in which the body is immersed – the 'accretion problem' as it subsequently became known. Lyttleton had the feeling that a formula in Eddington's book *The Internal Constitution of the Stars* gave considerably too small a rate. The upshot of our conversation was that I agreed to take a look at the thing. It was from this problem that my shift to astronomy from theoretical physics began. It did not take long to see that Eddington's calculation was correct for disconnected lumps of material, but for a gas in which internal collisions were important the accretion rate could be much higher than one would suspect from Eddington's formula, just as Lyttleton had hoped might be the case. Although we were to make a wrong immediate use of the discovery, which caused us some unpopularity in astronomical circles for a while, the technical details as they were developed from that time, especially in collaboration a few years later with Hermann Bondi, have proved their worth in later years. Today there is hardly an issue of any astronomical journal that does not contain a paper concerned with some aspect of the accretion problem.

This was a sideline, however, over the first six months of 1939. My Goldsmiths' exhibition would soon be running out, and if I was to continue in research at Cambridge I had to bestir myself once more, especially with regard to the possibility of securing a College Fellowship. The time had come therefore for me to stitch the various bits of research I had done into an essay. I submitted my achievements, such as they were, for the annual Fellowship competition at St John's College. My tutor, P.W. Wood, wanted me to submit also for the

Fellowship awarded annually at Emmanuel. Although it might have seemed rather like turning my back on my old college, I decided after some heart-searching to restrict my application to St John's, which was one of the few colleges whose Fellowships were freely open to any graduate of Cambridge or Oxford (within certain age limits). I knew John Cockroft personally from the Cavendish meetings I have described earlier, and I knew Dirac a little. Both were Fellows of St John's, whereas I knew no physicist who could speak for me at Emmanuel. John's gave three or four Fellowships, against only one from Emmanuel, and competing for a single award against candidates in all subjects (arts as well as science) had to be a chancy business.

On the St John's application form there was a question asking if one were a candidate also at another college. I knew this, because I had already applied both at St John's and Emmanuel in the previous year, and had been turned down for a Fellowship by both colleges. In the case of St John's, Cockroft told me I had been turned down because it was thought that Emmanuel would elect me. In 1939 I didn't want to fall between those same two stools again, so I confined my application this time to St John's, and as it happened was appointed to a Fellowship there for three years from May 1939.

I had also applied for a prestigious award offered by the Commission for the Exhibition of 1851, and to my astonishment, a week or two after the Fellowship, I was successful in obtaining a Senior Exhibition, which paid £600 per year for two years. Since the St John's Fellowship was worth £250 per year, plus accommodation and dinners, I now had the enormous sum of £850 per year, with little in the way of living expenses to worry about. But let the reader not be envious of my apparent good fortune, because in May 1939 the storm clouds of war were gathering in earnest. Soon I would be postponing both the Fellowship and the Exhibition until the end of the 1939–45 war. When I returned to Cambridge in 1945 to take them up again, the income of £850 a year would have declined to about one-third of its 1939 value. And by then I would have a wife and two children to support.

Shortly after inveigling me into the Secretaryship of the Delta-Squared V Club, Maurice Pryce left Cambridge to take up a lectureship at Liverpool University. If I was to retain my student status with the Inland Revenue, another research supervisor was therefore needed. Pryce suggested Dirac, so I went to Dirac and explained the position. Although normally he didn't accept students, Dirac broke his rule on this occasion because he simply couldn't resist the circular counter-logic of a supervisor who didn't want a research student who didn't want a supervisor.

Dirac didn't seem too much amused by farce or repartee, but he liked this kind of mental contretemps. The time I saw him laugh most was a year or two later when I told him the following story, after I had returned from my first visit to the United States. During the war you had to have a priority (of which there were, I believe, four grades) in order to travel on the US internal airlines. If you wanted to make a journey and you had a priority higher than someone else on an already-full plane (they were always full) you simply took the fellow's place and he was bounced off. One day a well-known scientist was travelling to give an important lecture, when unfortunately for him he was bounced by a general. It was unfortunate also for the general, because he was travelling to hear the lecture.

More than any other person I have known, Dirac raised the meaning of words and of syntax to a level of precision that was mathematical in its accuracy. He had nothing at all of the irritating habit of attempting to read hidden significance into your remarks. He paid everybody the compliment of supposing they knew exactly what they were saying, a compliment he sometimes took to extreme lengths. There was a time during the 1939–45 war when the British government was fencing with the American government to get as deeply as possible into the 'Manhattan' nuclear bomb-making project. The clarion call rang out in Whitehall to get Dirac involved as a bargaining-counter with the Americans. I did not witness the occasion myself, but I have it on good authority that the Minister concerned, Sir John Anderson, telephoned Dirac in Cambridge to ask if he would call at the Ministerial office when next in London. Dirac said that he would. Sir John then went on to ask as an afterthought how often Dirac was in London, to which Dirac replied: 'Oh, about once a year.'

Those scientists who moved first into what was called 'war work' quickly took up the most influential positions. The Cavendish began moving already in the summer of 1939, a few months ahead of the actual outbreak of war on 3 September 1939. Considering my close connections with the Cavendish six months earlier, it would have been natural for me to have gone along with such people as John Cockroft and Philip Dee. The reasons I didn't do so were personal; they would lead to my marriage on 28 December 1939.

My life had now entered its second act, and to this point the actor, or rather the actress, who was to prove the most important character in the plot had not appeared on stage. It happened quite without plan and quite without warning, as everything which turns out to be important always does. The point is that if you try to plan your life, nothing important can happen because it is impossible to conceive of what turns out to be really important. The crucial aspects of our lives can only come out of nowhere.

There was one undergraduate friend who had not passed into the shadows, because he was, and is still, an excellent correspondent. Richard Beetham had been one of the mathematics students in Emmanuel whom I had joined when I made the switch from natural sciences in October 1933. Now in May 1939 he wrote from a northern school where he had taken a post teaching mathematics to say that he would be visiting Cambridge at his half-term and would I meet him at such-and-such a time in the Dorothy Café. The Dot was a place the size of a ballroom situated on the upper floor of Hawkins, a confectioner with a big shop on the first floor. It was a popular resort for undergraduates, with the Whim Café taking its place for us research students. Hawkins is everlastingly associated in my mind with the composer Brahms. Shameful to relate, I once had an argument with Ray Bell of the Treasury as to the relative merits of Mozart and Brahms, with Bell, as befitted a Treasury man, taking Mozart's side. Overhearing our argument, another chap supported Bell, saying the tune of the Scherzo in the Brahms fourth symphony sounded to him as if Brahms could do no better than say to himself: 'Shall we go to Hawkins? No!' The remark did Brahms in for me, a position of which Tchaikovsky would have approved.

Anyway, I made my way to the Dot within a minute or two of the time Beetham had given me – I think it was 11.00 a.m. Surveying the many tables, I picked him out from the throng by the wave of his arm, and as I approached his table I saw two girls there. They had been his pupils. Jeanne Clark was taking a teacher's training course at Homerton College and her younger sister, Barbara, had come to Cambridge for an interview at Girton College. Instantly I knew that the important actress in the play which constituted my life was suddenly, and wholly unexpectedly, on stage. There was little to be done about it there and then, for the solid reason that a chap whom everybody called Percy, the presiding genius of the Dot with a big round face and big round spectacles, now began to thunder away on the piano and boom out the latest jazz hits. But a little before that day I had bought my first car, a twelve horsepower Rover of the 1936 vintage. It had cost £125, which was a lot to pay when you could pick up a tolerable second-hand car for £20, but my parents had always insisted that unless you can afford a really good article, don't buy at all.

A while later I had a licence to drive alone, and the Rover somehow found its way north to Richard Beetham's school. Barbara of the long plaits seemed mostly astonished that I apparently thought so little of my well-being as to have holes in the soles of my shoes, just as I had much earlier. Even so, I managed to persuade her to make a trip in the second half of August to the Lake District. Two days after leaving her, on 30 July 1939, I wrote my first letter to my future wife:

10 de Freville Ave.,
Cambridge.

Dear Barbara,

I forgot to ask your postal address. Don't be surprised at this, I never do anything right.

After leaving you I decided to pay a short visit to an old friend living in Sheffield who writes me periodically asking me to come and stay with him.

I am sending this to the school, and would you send to my address giving yours, so that when I have the preparations made I can let you know?

Fred

So having arranged to go on holiday with a girl, I had contrived not to discover her address, nor to leave her with mine.

Mid-August 1939 came round and the two of us drove off for the Lake District. We had intended to stop the first night at Buckden in Wharfedale, but the inn there was full. We continued to Hubberholme and Oughtershaw Moss, by exactly the same tiny road that Fred Jackson,

Edward Foster and I had walked some five years earlier. We stayed that night at a quiet old inn beyond Hawes, where four months later we would spend our honeymoon.

Barbara had arranged also to visit friends in Cheshire. We drove there from the Lake District, after which I continued to Bingley. Four days later, at the very end of August, I drove again to Cheshire to pick up Barbara and take her back home. A few miles along the road we stopped on a grassy verge. The news on the radio had been consistently bad. However much we wanted to believe otherwise, it was clear now that war was coming. War would change everything. It would destroy my comparative affluence. It would swallow my best creative period, just as I was finding my feet in research. But it also made a nonsense out of the two or three years of courtship that was considered proper in those days. On the grassy bank somewhere in Cheshire – I was never able to find the exact spot again – we decided to marry forthwith. More precisely, we would marry as soon as Barbara's parents could be accommodated to the idea.

The wedding was held early on 28 December 1939. The after-wedding ceremonies being over by 2.00 p.m., we set off to chase the light of the short winter day, through Doncaster, Leeds and Skipton. The roads became icy, and trying to hurry I had a bad skid between Skipton and Settle. Fortunately there was no other traffic on the road. Crossing the moor after Clapham, Ingleborough came in sight at last, glowing pink in the last moment of sunshine, with snow on its upper slopes. Not long afterwards we were at our destination, with a bright fire in the little sitting room to welcome us.

The war had come everywhere to the towns and cities, but it had still to reach up into those Yorkshire dales. The ten days we spent there were to be the last surviving breath of the old pre-war world. The inn was run then by a middle-aged couple. It would be twenty years on before we would stay in the same place again, by which time a younger generation of the family would have taken over. But the old man was still around. One day he looked hard at us, saying: 'I remember you now. You were the honeymoon couple who came just after the beginning of the war.' We had tried to hide our honeymoon status. When I asked the old man how he'd known, he just hopped away along the passageway that led from the kitchen to the main outer door, chuckling to himself.